CHICKOPEDIA

HENS AND COCKERELS

Facts and Fiction from A to Z

CHARLOTTE POPESCU

Moulton College

T 3 8 6 7 0

© Charlotte Popescu 2010

Published by Cavalier Paperbacks 2010

Cavalier Paperbacks
Burnham House,
Upavon,
Wilts SN9 6DU

www.cavalierpaperbacks.co.uk

This book is sold subject to the condition that it shall not, by way of trade or otherwise, be lent, re-sold, hired out, or otherwise circulated without the publisher's prior consent in any form of binding or cover other than that in which it is published and without a similar condition including this condition being imposed on the subsequent purchaser.

ISBN 978-1-899470-31-0

Printed and bound in Great Britain by Cromwell Press Group, White Horse Business Park, Trowbridge, Wiltshire BA14 OXB

FOREWORD

My passion is keeping hens in the garden; I also love doing research so I've compiled this A to Z guide on all things chicken-related including history, fiction, folklore, folktales, famous chickens, breeds and tips on keeping hens and cockerels, dealing with broodies, raising chicks and information on egg laying and eggs. There are details on over 60 pure breeds as well as on the hybrids. In all there are over 280 entries in this book.

Keeping hens is so rewarding – they add colour and interest to any garden, each hen has her own individual characteristics regardless of her breed; they will entertain you and provide you with that added bonus of fresh eggs.

In this book facts and fiction are mixed up together but fictional entries are represented by a mythological beast called the cockatrice or basilisk

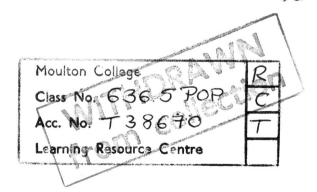

Moulton College

Class No. 636.5 POP

Acc. No. T 38670

Learning Resource Centre

R
C
T

WITHDRAWN from collection

A

 AESOP'S FABLES

The Fighting Cock and the Eagle

A cock who had got the worst of a fight with his rival for the favours of the hens, went and hid in a dark corner, while the victor climbed onto a high wall and crowed at the top of his voice. Immediately an eagle swooped down and snatched him up. The other was safe in his dark hiding place and was now able to woo the hens without fear of interruption. The moral – God resists the proud but gives grace to the humble.

The Cock and the Jewel

A barnyard cock while scratching up his dunghill came upon a jewel. 'Oh why,' said he, 'should I find this glistening thing? If some jeweller had found it he would have been beside himself with joy at the thought of its value: but to me it is no manner of use, nor do I care one jot about it; why, I would rather have one grain of barley than all the jewels in the world.'

The Cat and the Hens

A cat heard that there were some sick hens on a farm. So he disguised himself as a doctor and presented himself there, complete with a bag of professional instruments. Outside the farmhouse he stood and called to the hens to ask how they were. 'Fine,' came the reply, 'if you will get off the premises.'

The Cat and the Cock

A cat wanted to find a good reason for killing and eating a cock which she had caught. She concluded that his crowing at night annoyed men and preventing them from sleeping. The cock's defence was that he did men a good turn by waking them to start work. Then the cat charged him with committing the sin of incest with his mother and sisters – the cock replied that this was also a useful service since it made the hens lay well. 'You are full of specious ideas,' said the cat; 'but that is no reason why I should go hungry.' So she ate him – showing how an evil nature is bent on wrongdoing with or without the cloak of a fair-sounding pretext.

The Hen and the Serpent's Eggs

A hen found some serpent's eggs which she hatched by carefully sitting on them. A swallow who had watched her said, 'You fool, why do you rear creatures that, once they are grown up, will make you the first victim of their evil doing.'

The Ass, the Cock and the Lion

An ass and a cock were in a shed. A hungry lion caught sight of the ass and was about to go in and eat him. But he took fright at the sound of the cock crowing (for people say that lions are afraid of cocks) and ran away. The ass roused to a lofty contempt of him for being afraid of a cock, went out to pursue him; but when they were some distance away the lion ate him up.

The Dog, the Cock and the Fox

A Dog and a Cock wished to see something of the world. So they left the farmyard and set out along the road that led to the woods. The two comrades travelled along in the very best of spirits. At nightfall the Cock, looking for a place to roost, spied nearby a

hollow tree that he thought would do very nicely. The Dog could creep inside and the Cock would fly up on one of the branches. So said, so done, and both slept very comfortably. With the first glimmer of dawn the Cock awoke. He thought he was still in the farmyard where he always aroused the household at daybreak. So standing on tip-toes he flapped his wings and crowed lustily. But instead of awakening the farmer, he awakened a Fox not far off. The Fox immediately had rosy visions of a very delicious breakfast. Hurrying to the tree where the Cock was roosting, he said: 'A hearty welcome to our woods, honoured sir. I cannot tell you how glad I am to see you here. I am sure we shall become friends.' 'I feel flattered, kind sir,' replied the Cock slyly. 'Please go around to the door of my house at the foot of the tree, my porter will let you in.' The hungry but unsuspecting Fox, went around the tree, and in a twinkling the Dog had seized him.

The Woman and the Fat Hen
A woman owned a hen that laid an egg every morning. Since the hen's eggs were of excellent quality, they sold for a good price. So at one point, the woman thought to herself, 'If I double my hen's allowance of barley, she'll lay twice a day.' Therefore she put her plan to work, and the hen became so fat and contented she stopped laying altogether.

AGE
Chickens can live for up to 10 years but are vulnerable from the start to predator attacks and diseases so their lives are not easy!

AIR SAC
This is a space between the egg and shell that gradually increases as the egg ages. This sac will develop at the top end of the egg;

usually eggs are stored with the fat end uppermost so this is where the air sac will be.

 ALAN-A-DALE

Alan-a-Dale was the lute playing rooster and musical narrator of Disney's animated *Robin Hood* (1973).

ALBUMEN

Albumen is just another name for egg white. It is rich in protein and vitamins and in biological terms supports and protects the egg yolk. Allegedly the Romans used egg white as glue.

ALDROVANDI

Ulisse Aldrovandi was born in Bologna in 1522 and was a professor of natural history at the university there. He wrote the first comprehensive book devoted to the chicken, covering all aspects including chicken cookery. He began his volume: 'No proof is required, for it is clear to all, how much benefit the cock and his wives provide for the human race. They furnish food for both humans who are well and those who are ill and rally those who are almost dead. Which condition of the body, both internal or external, does not obtain remedies from the chicken? … The cock and the hen, desirous of generating offspring, make their genus eternal under the leadership of nature.' Aldrovandi believed that many parts of the cockerel could be used to alleviate diseases. There is a street named after him in Rome on which there is a luxury hotel, the Aldrovandi Palace Villa Borghese in the Borghese Gardens.

 ALECTORII

The Romans believed that crystalline stones, called alectorii, could

be found in the gizzards of cockerels. These were thought to have magical properties so that anyone possessing them would be endowed with courage, strength and success with money and women.

ALECTROMANCY or ALECTRYOMANCY

Alectromancy is a brand of clairvoyancy which relied on cockerels to predict the future or act as an oracle. A circle would be drawn in the earth with parts divided by letters of the alphabet. Grain was placed on each letter. A white cockerel would be placed in the circle and the letters from which he pecked grain would be written down in order. These would supposedly make up the name of a person important to an inquiry.

ALECTRYOMACHY or ALECTOROMACHY

This is a little known word for cockfighting. 'Alectryo' means cockerel and 'machy' means battle in Greek.

 ALECTRYON

Ares, God of War, posted a Greek youth as a guard by the door when he visited Aphrodite, Goddess of Love. Alectryon fell asleep during the night so that their lovemaking was discovered by Helios, the Sun God. As punishment, the boy was turned into a cock which since then has never stopped announcing the arrival of the sun. The Greek word Alectryon means cockerel – that which gets you out of bed (lektron). There is a genus of trees of the Soapberry family Sapindaceae called Alectryon – so called because of the cockscomb appearance of the aril on the fruit.

ALEKTOROPHOBIA
A fear of chickens and other birds.

ALLOTMENT HENS
Hens are allowed on all Council owned allotments in England and Wales. The 1950 Allotment Act states that hens and rabbits are permitted livestock although cockerels are not allowed. This can be restricted in some cases by local by-laws.

AMERICAN BREEDS Named after places
Rhode Island Red, New Hampshire Red and the Jersey Giant are all named after US states. The Plymouth Rock is named after the Plymouth Rock in Massachusetts. The Delaware was developed in Delaware in 1940 from barred Plymouth Rock males and New Hampshire Red hens. All these breeds come from states in north east America and predominantly from the New England states. See separate entries under individual breeds

ANCIENT GREEK CHICKENS
The cockerel was sacred to Athena, goddess of wisdom and warfare – she was depicted with a cockerel on her helmet. To Demeter, goddess of agriculture and her daughter Persephone the cockerel symbolised fertility. He was connected with Helios, the Sun God because of his crowing at dawn. Ganymede, Zeus's young lover, was often depicted with a cockerel in his hand. Aside from the cockerels being used for religious and fighting purposes it was the Egyptians who introduced the

Greeks to keeping chickens for meat and eggs (the Egyptians were well advanced in farming and animal husbandry – see incubation).

Greeks on Cockerels:

Aristophanes in *The Birds* wrote: 'Just like the great king he struts along, the only bird that has a straight crest on his head.'

Themistocles (524 – 460BC) led his troops against the Persians saw two cocks fighting and roused the courage of his soldiers by pointing out the obstinacy with which the cocks fought.

Plato laments: 'Not only boys but men breed fighting cocks and use a lot of time up in similar idle amusements.'

According to Plato in *Phaedo*, Socrates' last words after he had drunk poison were: 'Crito, we owe a cock to Aesculapius – please don't forget to pay the debt.'

Greeks on Hens:

Aristotle wrote extensively on chickens in his *History of Animals*. He had a theory on the Chicken and the Egg – he argued that the chicken comes before the egg – a chicken must already exist for the egg to be a potential chicken. We cannot point to an object and say that is a chicken egg if there is no such thing as a chicken. He was the first to study the embryonic development of the egg which he opened and described on each day of its incubation.

When Alcibiades asked Socrates why he didn't turn out his shrewish wife, Socrates said: 'Why don't you drive out hens that are noisy with their wings?' Alcibiades: 'Because they lay eggs.' Socrates: 'A wife bears children for me.'

Oppian of Apamea wrote in his *On Hunting* around 200AD: 'With how much love the joyful hen nourishes her tender chicks. If

11

she sees a hawk, descending, cackling in a loud voice, her feathers raised high, her neck curved back she spreads her swelling wings over the clucking chicks. Then the frightened chick chirps and hides himself under these high walls and the fearful mother gathers the long line of chicks under her plumage. Careful mother that she is, she attacks the daring hawk and frees her dear chicks from the mouth of the rapacious bird and warms her featherless young; deprived of hair they leave their festive nests in shining brightness.'

Greeks on Hens and Cockerels:

Aelian wrote in O*n Animals*: 'There is a temple to Heracles and to his wife Hebe. Now they say that in the precincts of these temples a large number of tame cockerels and hens are kept. They feed and consort together according to their sex, are fed at the public expense and are consecrated to the two gods. The hens feed in the temple of Hebe while their mates feed in the temple of Heracles. And a never-failing channel of clear water flows between them. Now on the one hand not one hen ever appears in the temple of Heracles. On the other hand at the season of mating, the cockerels fly across the channel and after consorting with the hens return to their own quarters at the side of the God whom they serve, cleansed by the water that separates the sexes. And so to begin with, as a natural result of this union eggs are laid; later on when the hens have warmed them and hatched the chicks, the cockerels carry off the male birds to rear them, while the hens make it their business to rear their daughters.'

ANCIENT ROMAN CHICKENS

From Greece chickens spread to Rome and were all-important.

Hens were domesticated and breeds were developed for meat and eggs. Chickens were sacred birds, used for medicine and as a subject for philosophical enquiry. The cockerel remained a central figure in religion. He was regarded as sacred to Mars, the God of War and was associated with Mercury, being the herald of a new day which symbolised his role as messenger. Hens were also used in sacrifices to Mercury. The cockerel was dedicated to Apollo, the Sun God. Chickens were used extensively by the Romans to predict the future. The right foot of a cock, as a talisman, was thought to enable a man to overcome his enemy. The ancients measured the passage of night and arrival of day by the cock's crowing (this was before sundials were widely used).

Romans on Hens:

In 249BC the Roman General, Publius Claudius Pulcher had the chickens thrown overboard when they refused to feed before the Battle of Drepana saying 'if they won't eat, perhaps they will drink'. He promptly lost his battle against the Carthaginians. It was a bad omen for battle if chickens did not eat when let out of their coop (this type of divination was called oraculum ex tripudio and the official in charge of looking after the sacred chickens was called the Pullarius).

Columella, Varro and Pliny all wrote extensively on their observations of chickens.

Varro (100AD) wrote a lot about chickens in *On Rural Matters* including information on breeds and bantams of different colours. He even mentioned battery cages for fattening poultry.

Pliny wrote about hens in his *Natural History*. He mentions the people of Delos who fattened hens from this revolting practice of

devouring fat birds basted in their own gravy. The Roman writers all agreed that one or two year old hens were the best for laying, taking care of their eggs and making good mothers. Amazingly, they said that hens laid most of the year, apart from two months and some even in midwinter (and they didn't have Layers Pellets)!

Romans on Cockerels:

Ovid, the poet, wrote, 'Now the light bringer treads the northern skies and the bird wakes wretched men to their work.'

Seneca gave us the proverb, 'Every Cock will Crow upon his own Dunghill' – he is referring to Claudius' deification and the pun is that Gallus was Latin for Gaul (Claudius's birthplace) as well as for cock.

Pliny said that cockfighting was an annual exhibition at Pergamus. Columella, writing in the 1st Century AD said that devotees spent their patrimony betting at the side of the cockpit.

Caesar talks about cockerels which are for diversion and pleasure. For History see also Cockerels

ANCONA

The Ancona hen, as the name suggests, originated in Ancona, Italy. Both the cockerel and hen, in large fowl and bantam, are similar in colour – a mottled black and white. The single comb on the female tends to flop over on one side. The hens lay white eggs and are similar to Leghorns.

ANDALUSIAN

This breed owes its name to the province of Andalusia in Spain and is one of the oldest Mediterranean breeds. The Andalusian is blue, probably developed from crossing black and white stock. The female has a distinctive comb which flops to one side of its head. She has white earlobes and lays white eggs. Large fowl and bantams are available.

 ## ANIMAL FARM by George Orwell (1945)

Animal Farm is a well known satire on communism. It is interesting to see what uses the hens and cockerels have in *Animal Farm*, although not considered the most intelligent of animals. The carthorse Boxer had an arrangement with the cockerels to call him half an hour earlier than anyone else so that he could put in extra work. The hens and ducks managed to save five bushels of corn at the harvest by gathering up any stray grains. The pig, Snowball, formed the Egg Production Committee. The animals were given reading and writing classes but it was 'found that the stupider animals such as the sheep, hens and ducks were unable to learn the Seven Commandments by heart' (the seven commandments were rules that the pigs had devised such as 'no animal shall wear clothes, sleep in a bed, drink alcohol or kill any other animal') – Snowball thus reduced the commandments to a single motto – 'Four legs good, two legs bad' – the birds naturally objected to this but Snowball insisted that their wings counted as legs.

After a bitter winter the animals were low on grain. Napoleon, pig dictator, had negotiated a contract for 400 eggs to be sold every week in order to pay for more grain and the hens were told

to give up their eggs. This created something close to a rebellion as the hens were 'just getting their clutches ready for the spring sitting'. Led by three Black Minorca pullets the hens tried to avoid Napoleon's decree. They flew onto the rafters and laid their eggs which smashed on the floor. In retaliation Napoleon stopped their rations. The hens held out for five days but then gave in and went back to their nesting boxes. Nine hens had died, though, their bodies were buried in the orchard and it was announced that they had died of coccidiosis. The eggs were thus duly delivered.

Later on in the story Napoleon appears less frequently in public but when he does he is accompanied not only by his retinue of dogs but by a black cockerel who marches in front of him and acts like a trumpeter, cock-a-doodle-dooing before Napoleon speaks.

Napoleon commanded that once a week the animals would hold a Spontaneous Demonstration to celebrate the ups and downs of life on Animal Farm – they would march around the boundary of the farm in military formation with the pigs leading followed by the horses, cows, sheep and lastly the poultry. The dogs would flank the procession and at the head, in front of the pigs, would march Napoleon's black cockerel.

APPENZELLER

Strictly speaking the Appenzeller is called Appenzeller Spitzhauben and was named after the local lace bonnets worn by the ladies of Appenzellerland in Switzerland. Spitzhauben actually means pointed bonnet and the crest on an Appenzeller also points forward, looking like a bonnet. These birds were imported into Britain relatively recently and have proved popular. Appenzellers come in three colours: silver-spangled, gold-spangled or black. They are particularly attractive and very striking. The cocks look magnificent

with their beautiful tail feathers and small head crests. This is a light soft-feathered breed which can be quite flighty. The hens lay white eggs. Appenzellers are quite small considering they are large fowl.

ARAUCANA

Araucanas were bred by the Indians from the Arauca Province of northern Chile in South America, who refused to let the Spanish conquerors crossbreed their hens. They are the only hens in the world to lay turquoise eggs (colours vary between green, olive and blue) but no one knows quite why they do. Araucanas are crested and have faces covered with thick muffling. They come in many colours including lavender, blue, silver, black and white. There is also a rumpless variation of the breed which, as the name suggests, does not have a tail but is favoured because it lays a large egg in relation to its body size. Large fowl and bantams are available.

ASIL (ASEEL)

The Asil is probably the oldest game fowl and was bred in India for its fighting qualities. The name Asil is Arabic for 'long pedigree'.

The Asil was extremely strong with a thick muscular neck and powerful legs; add to that a belligerent temperament and one had a superb fighting cock.

AUSTRALORP

The Australorp was developed from the Black Orpington in Australia. The name originated from The Austral Orpington Club which was set up for them in the 1920s. The idea was to create a good egg layer but also to retain the meat quality of the Orpington. Hens are excellent layers of tinted eggs. Australorps remain black with a brilliant green sheen but there is also a blue variety; the breed is smaller and neater than the Orpington. A bantam version is available.

AUTOSEXING

Autosexing is the practice of breeding chicks, which can be sexed as soon as they hatch by their differing down colouring. The autosexing breeds are pure breeds (i.e. they breed true) so whichever way they are crossed, father to daughter, mother to son etc. males and females can be distinguished at birth. Sex-linked birds are different – Rhode Island Red (gold) can be crossed with light Sussex (silver) and the chicks can be sexed at birth but this will not work for the second generation. There are various autosexing breeds that have been developed, their names ending in –bar. The first of these was the Cambar and was a cross between the Gold Campine and the barred Plymouth Rock. The barring is sex-linked and there is a double dose in the male and a single dose in the female – this means the male chick is paler with a blurred pattern of markings compared to the female chick. Recognised breeds are

the Gold, Silver and Cream Legbar (the Cream Legbar is a crossing which involves the Araucana and therefore lays blue eggs); the Rhodebar (from Rhode Island Red); Welbar (from Welsummer) and Dorbar (from Dorking). The Wybar uses the laced Wyandotte with the barred Plymouth Rock and is most commonly in silver but they are rare. The Brussbar is also rare and is the autosexing version of the Brown Sussex. The crested Cream Legbars have been used to breed a blue egg-laying hybrid called Columbine or Skyline. These birds are typically reddish brown partridge feathered, some with crest and some without. They usually have quite a large comb but the probability of blue egg colour from these hybrids is usually 85%. There is also now a Silbar (from a Silkie).

AVIAN FLU

This is the highly contagious viral disease affecting respiratory, digestive and/or the nervous system of many species of wild and domesticated birds. The H5N1 strain of Avian Flu surfaced in south east Asia in 2004 and started to spread. Transfers to domestic poultry occurred in Europe but with early detection and control the outbreak was eradicated. Symptoms include swelling of the head, comb and wattles turning blue, lethargy, loss of appetite, respiratory stress, diarrhoea and a drop in egg production.

Anyone suspecting an outbreak amongst their flock must immediately inform DEFRA.

B

BADGERS

Badgers operating at night will kill and eat any hen that is susceptible – i.e. sitting on eggs in a secret location. Badgers can easily burrow under normal fences and break their way into hen houses through any weak spots as they are strong and determined. They can also lift vertical pop holes with their snout and undo easy latches. Bolts however will defeat them. Unlike foxes who will kill a whole flock, the badger will only kill one hen per night and eat most of the carcass on the spot.

BANTAM

Bantam is the name of a town and district in Java. In 1595 the Dutch established themselves there and in 1602 the English were dominant in Java. The locals sold the native jungle fowl from Bantam to the British who took them back to England. They became very popular and eventually the word Bantam was used to describe all small poultry including what are also known as miniatures. Later Pekin bantams were imported from China and Japanese bantams were imported from Japan – these are true bantams with no large counterparts. Other true bantams are the Belgian, Booted, Dutch, Nankin, Rosecomb, Sebright and Tuzo. Many bantams have been developed from breeds of large fowl. These birds or miniatures should be 25% the size of the equivalent large fowl.

BARN EGGS

Barn eggs are laid by hens kept in a barn system. Birds are kept inside large sheds all day so never see the light of day, at a density of between nine and 12 hens per square metre. They can at least move around, flap their wings and fly. They have nest boxes and some have perches and platforms. Hens in this sort of accommodation have been likened to a crowded football terrace. The British Egg Information Service states that 4% of the total number of eggs produced are from barn hens.

BARNEVELDER

The Barnevelder is a Dutch breed which originated in the town of Barneveld in Holland. Most farmers in that area were keeping poultry as early as the 12th Century. Around 1850 the poultry there were crossed with imported stock such as Cochins, Malays, Brahmas and Langshans and the value of selection for utility was discovered – egg production improved substantially and brown eggs were the preferred colour. The result by 1900 was the Barnevelder. The inhabitants of Barneveld always claimed that their chickens laid 313 eggs – being a religious community with no work being done on Sundays that meant 365 days minus 52 Sundays. However this was a little optimistic – egg production is more likely to be about 200 eggs a year. Barnevelders, as might be expected, are the most popular dual-purpose breed in Holland – the climate there is often cold, windy and damp. This made Barnevelders a thrifty and hardy breed and very suitable for the similar climate in Britain. Barnevelders were imported into Britain in the early 1900s. The hens nowadays are good layers of dark brown eggs. Maranses were used to improve the dark brown colour of the eggs. Colour variations in the birds are double-laced with black and brown (the

most popular), black, partridge and silver. This is a heavy soft-feathered breed and the bantams are replicas of their large fowl counterparts. Back in Holland Barnevelder hens have certainly helped the development of their native town, Barneveld, where poultry, eggs and associated products are still a major source of income in the area. The Dutch Poultry Museum is based there as is the International Barneveld College, an educational poultry institute.
See Dutch Poultry Museum

 BASILISK

The basilisk was a mythical monster, hatched by a cockerel from a serpent's egg, which from the Middle Ages was depicted as a snake with the head and legs of a cockerel. The word Basilisk came from the Greek for little king, Basiliscus. This monster could kill by its breath, smell or just its look. But if it looked in a mirror and saw its own image it would die or would drop dead at the crow of a cockerel. In heraldry the basilisk was represented with the head, torso and feet of a cockerel, the tongue and rump of a snake and the wings of a bat.
See also Cockatrice

BATTERY EGGS (EGGS FROM CAGED HENS)
In the UK eggs are consumed at the rate of 29 million per day. Figures in 2010 suggest that 58% of eggs are from battery hens. There are 28 million hens in all systems laying an average of 314 eggs per year. The battery hens are expected to lay six eggs per week but cannot keep this intensive laying up for more than a year, which is when they are sent for slaughter.
See also Barn Eggs, Free Range and Organic Eggs

BATTERY HENS AND CAGES

Battery cages were first used for laying hens in the 1930s. At this time one bird was kept in each cage. After the war cages became more prevalent and several birds were confined in one cage. Their top beaks were trimmed making it difficult to damage each other by pecking; hens were stimulated by light to lay continuously and after one year they were sent to the slaughterhouse. If battery hens were kept for a second season it would be natural for them to moult after a year of laying and this would take around eight weeks. Instead the lights would be turned off and feeding halted – this would stimulate a quick moult so that hens could start laying again. This practice has now stopped, at least in the UK.

Today hens, which are most commonly a hybrid variety called ISA Brown (a cross between Rhode Island Red and Rhode Island White) are still kept in cages with four or five birds in an area of 50 x 50cm (each hen has a space just over the size of an A4 sheet of paper). The cages have sloping wire floors so the birds cannot sit, flap their wings or do anything apart from laying, eating and drinking. The cages form long rows and are stacked in several tiers. The industrial units in which these cages are housed are artificially lit and ventilated. Caged birds never experience fresh air or natural light. At present the tips of their beaks are still cut off (see beak tipping). From 2012 all hens in Europe will have to be kept in enriched cages, which will be only slightly bigger (they will have just under 2 x A4 sheets of paper as space).

Battery hens are sent to slaughter when they are eighteen months old after a year of intensive laying. At this point they can be rescued (see ex-batteries) but they may have inherent problems such as broken bones and twisted claws. At present there are around 18 million hens being kept in battery cages in Britain. In 2009 it is

estimated that around 100,000 battery hens were rescued and rehomed by the various large and smaller rescue centres.

BATTERY HEN WELFARE TRUST

The Battery Hen Welfare Trust became the UK's first registered charity for laying hens in 2005 and was established in order to raise awareness for the millions of hens kept in cages in the UK. The charity was started by Jane Howorth who decided to champion the plight of the battery hen. Howorth, based in Devon, began rescuing battery hens from slaughter for her own enjoyment. In October 2003 and several hundred hens later she decided to take 100 hens from a local battery farm in Devon with the specific purpose of finding them good homes. Since then thousands of hens have been rescued from slaughter and given the opportunity to enjoy a free range retirement. Most go on to become family pets. The long-term aim of the charity is to diminish consumer demand for battery eggs whilst at the same time promoting British farmers who use welfare friendly systems. The charity encourages consumers to buy products containing only British free range, organic or barn eggs. In 2009 the trust rescued around 60,000 hens.

BEAK PIGMENT

This only occurs in yellow skinned breeds such as Leghorns, Wyandottes and Rhode Island Reds – white-skinned breeds such as Sussex and Orpington do not show pigment. The pigment is yellow, called xantophylls and is obtained from yellow maize and green plants. When a hen starts laying her beak will be full of pigment as will her legs and feet. As she continues laying the pigment, which starts at the base, gradually fades as it is required for the yolks. It

will be seen as a ring of pigment in the middle of her beak when she is laying and will gradually fade until the beak looks bleached. When the hen stops laying the pigment will gradually reappear.

BEAK TIPPING

Beak tipping or debeaking is a cruel practice common in battery hens – hens use the tips of their beaks for pecking, preening and to manipulate and investigate as they don't have hands! The tip is also very sensitive.

Most commonly now in the UK an infra-red beam is used to burn the chicks' beaks so that one third of the length of the beak dies and falls off. Another method is to cut off a third of the beak with a red-hot blade (and this may be used to re-cut the beak when the hen is older); it is thought that the hen does suffer pain as the beak has nerves and blood vessels, (this is not like cutting finger or toe nails). The top beak is therefore shortened leaving the bottom beak sticking out. This procedure is carried out to stop battery hens from pecking and harming each other. Once a hen has been debeaked the tip of the beak is unlikely to fully grow back; although in younger birds the beak will grow as the bird grows but will always remain blunted. The UK Government has proposed banning debeaking from January 2011 but this is an ongoing debate.

BEARD

A beard is a conglomeration of feathers under the throat of some breeds such as the Faverolles, Houdan, Belgian Bearded Bantam and some varieties of Poland.

See also Muffling

BEDDING

Various bedding can be used in hen houses. Wood shavings or sawdust are best – any moisture from droppings is absorbed. Straw is cheaper but can result in feathers being stained. Shredded paper can also be used. Hay should not be used as it harbours harmful mould spores that can cause breathing problems. All bedding should be changed once a week.

BELGIAN BEARDED BANTAMS

Three varieties are standardised in Britain: Barbu d'Uccle (Bearded Uccle) is, as the name suggests, heavily feathered around the neck with feathered feet. It has a single comb and comes in many colour variations including black-mottled, lavender, porcelaine, millefleur and laced-blue. The amazing choice of colours is probably unrivalled in any other breed. Barbu d'Anvers (Bearded Antwerp) differs from the Barbu d'Uccle in that it has clean legs, a rose comb and in the males the wings are carried very low, almost vertically. Barbu de Watermael (Bearded Watermael) is crested and clean-legged, small and perky. All three remind one of a human wearing an overcoat with the collar turned up. These are some of the oldest true bantam breeds. A Dutch painting from the 17th Century by Albert Cuyp reveals a small hen with similar markings to a quail-coloured Barbu d'Anvers. Belgian bearded bantam hens lay small cream eggs.

BILLINA

Billina is a yellow talking hen featuring in *Ozma to Oz*, Frank Baum's sequel to *The Wizard of Oz*. Billina is shipwrecked with Dorothy Gale – they end up on a chicken coop which has been flung off a ship in a violent storm on its way to Australia. '…She kept tight hold of the stout slats and as soon as she could get the water out of her eyes she saw that the wind had ripped the cover from the coop, and the poor chickens were fluttering away in every direction, being blown by the wind until they looked like feather dusters without handles … a strange noise awakened her. Surely it was a hen cackling! … 'Why, I've just laid an egg, that's all,' replied a small, but sharp and distinct voice, and looking around her the little girl discovered a yellow hen squatting in the opposite corner of the coop.

'Dear me!' she exclaimed, in surprise; 'Have you been here all night, too?'

'Of course,' answered the hen, fluttering her wings and yawning. 'When the coop blew away from the ship I clung fast to this corner, with claws and beak, for I knew if I fell into the water I'd surely be drowned...

'May I inquire your name, ma'am?' asked the little girl.

'My name is Bill,' said the yellow hen, somewhat gruffly.

'Bill! Why, that's a boy's name.'

'What difference does that make?'

'You're a lady hen, aren't you?' 'Of course. But when I was first hatched out no one could tell whether I was going to be a hen or a rooster; so the little boy at the farm called me Bill, and made a pet of me because I was the only yellow chick in the whole brood.

When I grew up, and he found that I didn't crow and fight, as all the roosters do, he did not think to change my name, and every creature in the barn-yard, as well as the people in the house, knew me as 'Bill.'

... 'If you don't mind, I shall call you 'Billina.' Putting the 'eena' on the end makes it a girl's name, you see.'

Soon after this Dorothy and Billina reach land and their adventures continue.

BLACK PULLET, THE

The Black Pullet, also known *as The Hen that lays Golden Eggs,* is a grimoire or magician's handbook. It is a guide to the construction and use of magical talismanic rings. With the use of these rings people attained the powers to produce the Black Pullet. Unlimited wealth was granted to whoever could create this incredible hen.

BLACK ROCK

Black Rocks are a true first cross hybrid, bred from selected strains of Rhode Island Reds and barred Plymouth Rocks. Peter Siddons of Muirfield Hatchery in Scotland acquired the breeding stock from breeders in America in 1973. He has been the sole breeder since then but is now handing over the reins to Eddie Lovett in Renfrewshire who will take over the hatchery business. The gold feathered genes of the Rhode Island Red are crossed with the silver feathered lines of the Plymouth Rock which produces a sex linkage feature that identifies each sex when the chicks hatch. This enables the hatchery to keep selected cockerels but they are not available for sale. The female chicks are sent out to the agents who

bring them on and sell them at POL (Point of Lay). Black Rocks have a good covering of feathers, which protect them in all weather conditions. They also have a highly developed immune system.

Black Rocks should not go broody as this trait has been bred out of them and although egg production is fantastic in the first two years, it may decrease thereafter. Black Rocks are hybrids that do manage to go on producing eggs as they get older and may live for up to ten years. They also produce good strong egg-shells and this reduces the chances of egg peritonitis which can occur in battery hens and some other commercial hybrids. Black Rocks are either black or ginger (ginger breast with attractive ginger and black lacing).

BLASTODERM AND BLASTODISC

Blastoderm is the germ on the egg yolk where the baby chick will begin to grow if the egg is fertile. It is located on the surface of the yolk and is a round white mark around 4mm in diameter. If the egg is infertile then this spot is called the blastodisc and is a more irregular shape and smaller at around 2mm in diameter.

BLOOD SPOTS

Sometimes small blood spots or rings can be seen on the edge of an egg yolk. Meat spots are similar but are brown-coloured and show up on the egg white. These spots are completely harmless. They are caused by the rupture of a blood vessel in the ovary, which may have occurred due to a sudden fright.

BLOOM

Bloom is the moist coating that can be seen on an egg when just laid but which then dries. This outer coating is also referred to as the cuticle and is responsible for keeping out bacteria. Bloom is also the sheen or gloss on the feathers of a hen or cockerel.

BLUE HEN STATE

A man from Delaware went to war during the American Revolution. He brought with him two fighting cocks for entertainment, saying they had been the chicks of a blue hen he had at home. These cocks were true fighters and were so fierce they caused quite a stir. The Delaware troops began boasting to the troops from other states that they could defeat any other fighting cocks. The motto of the Delaware troops became, 'We're the Blue Hen's chickens. We will fight to the end.' And the other men took to calling the Delaware men the Blue Hen's Chicks; today Delaware is still known as the Blue Hen State. In 1939 the Blue Hen Chicken was voted the official Delaware state bird.

BOOTED BANTAM (Sablepoot)

The Booted Bantam or Sablepoot, as it is called in Holland, is an ancient breed. It was crossed with the Belgian Barbu d'Anvers to

create the Barbu d'Uccle. The Booted Bantam has no muffling but does have feathered feet. These bantams can be black, white, millefleur or porcelaine and lay small tinted eggs.

BRAHMA

The Brahma is a very old breed supposedly from India and early pictures show that it was very similar to the Cochin. The name Brahma is taken from the river Brahmaputra in India. However, it is now generally agreed that the Brahma was created in America from Shanghais or Cochins imported from China in the 1800s and crossed with Grey Chittagongs (Malay type birds from India). Brahmas were sent to Queen Victoria in 1852 and thus the breed was introduced to Britain.

They have distinctive feathered legs and feet and pea combs. They come in a variety of colours including dark, buff, light, birchen and dark Columbian. Brahmas are very large – they have a sort of majestic massiveness  and have been variously described as 'noble and commanding', 'intelligent looking', 'with a neck well proportioned and finely curved as in a spirited horse'. Buff Brahmas are probably the most popular variety but can weigh from 5 to 6kg so are not ideal for small children. They do need space but, because they don't fly, are easy to keep in a run. The Brahma is a heavy, soft-feathered breed and hens lay tinted eggs. They have been used in the creation of many new breeds and in developing new colours in existing ones. See Victoria, Queen

BRESSE CHICKENS

La Bresse chickens are French table birds bred specifically for meat which is traditionally marbled with fat. The birds are white with blue feet.

BRITISH BREEDS Named after places

The Sussex is named after the county as is the Norfolk Grey and Derbyshire Redcap. The Dorking is named after the town in Surrey. The Orpington is named after a village in Kent where the breed was developed, as is the Ixworth named after a village in Suffolk. See separate entries under individual breeds

BROODER

A brooder is used to rear chicks that have been hatched in an incubator. A heat lamp will keep the chicks warm and they will need to stay in a brooder until they develop a reasonable amount of feathers at between four and six weeks.

BROODIES

Hens generally go broody (wanting to produce chicks) after they have laid between 12 and 20 eggs if their eggs are left in their nests. Each hen warms her eggs every time she sits to lay an egg and sits longer as the time for broodiness approaches. Collecting the eggs every day prevents a hen going broody as easily. Hens that go persistently broody are the little Pekins, Silkies and the heavier breeds such as Orpingtons and Brahmas. Wyandottes also tend to go broody quite frequently. Hens may become broody two or three times in the spring and summer.

Classic symptoms of a broody hen are: firmly sitting on the nest

box, reluctant to move, fluffing up her feathers, clucking and trying to peck anyone lifting her off as she doesn't like her eggs interfered with. She may also have plucked feathers from her chest and inner legs to feather her nest and allow her eggs to get closer to her warm body. When out of the nest box she will walk around, puffed up, clucking and behaving in a bad tempered way. She will eat and drink and then try to get back to her nest. If shut out she will sit outside on the bare ground, picking up twigs and straw and throwing over them over her back, often enduring pecks from other hens.

To stop a hen being broody, she should be put in an airy coop with a slatted or wire mesh floor where there is no opportunity for nesting. Ideally this coop should be raised off the ground as the air circulating around will lower her body temperature and stop her feeling broody. Other ideas include dunking her in cold water or putting ice cubes under her. These methods may need to be repeated several times.

If a hen goes broody on eggs she has laid in her own nest, she will automatically make her own storage conditions. Brooding is quite a secretive process for a hen and she will have chosen the darkest corner that she can find. If she is allowed to free range this could mean she has made a nest hidden away in the undergrowth in the corner of a garden, where she may have laid a substantial number of eggs. If there is a cockerel and so plenty of fertile eggs and one of the hens has gone broody but all her eggs have been collected in the days beforehand then a number of fertile eggs need to be put under her at the same time. If a hen has gone broody in an unsuitable spot (she could be vulnerable to predators) she and her eggs will need to be moved to a safe nesting box. This can be tricky; she may not be happy and may return to the old nest – it is

best done at dusk and she should be watched the next day when she comes off her nest to feed and drink to make sure she returns to her new nest.

BROWN EGGS VERSUS WHITE EGGS

The British prefer brown, the Americans white eggs. JB Priestley wrote an essay, *The Meaning of Brown Eggs,* in which he said 'Americans despise brown eggs because they seem closer to nature' whilst white eggs are better, 'especially if given to precious children because their very whiteness suggests hygiene and purity.' After the war the British believed that white eggs were less nutritious like white bread – a pure fallacy! So farmers selected brown egg laying breeds. In the US the favoured white egg layer was the Leghorn. EB White, the American essayist, wrote in response to Priestley: 'I ascribe the whole business [preference for white eggs] to a busy little female – the White Leghorn hen. She is nervous, she is flighty, she is the greatest egg-machine on two legs and it just happens that she lays a white egg. She's never too distracted to do her job. If she were on her way to a fire, she would pause long enough to lay an egg. This endears her to the poultrymen of America, who are out to produce the greatest number of eggs for the least money paid out for feed ...'

BUMBLEFOOT

This can be caused by a chicken damaging its foot when it jumps down from a perch which is too high. There will be a round swelling, which looks not unlike a corn or wart on the pad of the foot.

C

CACKLEBERRY

Cackleberries, chickenberries, hen fruit or chicken fruit are all slang words for eggs.

CAMPINE

The Campine is an ancient breed from Antwerp in Belgium which has a very attractive barring or pencilling on the feathers, although the neck is without markings. Bred in silver or gold in large fowl and bantam, the Campine was used to produce pencilled Hamburghs. More recently it has been used in the production of the first autosexing breed, the Cambar. Campine hens lay a good number of smallish white eggs; they are lively, quite flighty, beautiful birds that like to free range.

CANDLING EGGS

Candling was originally done by holding the egg up to the light of a candle to check on embryo growth. Nowadays a candler with a light bulb attached can be bought. This is basically a concentrated source of light so that one can see through the shell and check the development of a chick. This can be done on the sixth or seventh day of incubation and on the seventeenth day and allows eggs to be discarded when the embryo has not developed. On the seventh day, if the egg is fertile, a dark shadow will be seen with veins running through it – it looks similar to a spider with red legs. An

infertile egg is clear and shows the light clearly through it. On the 17th day fertile eggs will show a dense black mass with a clearly defined air cell at the broad end.

CAPON

A capon is a castrated cockerel. A surgical procedure has to be carried out to remove the testes. The cockerel may still crow but his comb and wattles will stop growing. A caponised cockerel will grow fat and when killed produces a unique meat which is tender and juicy. It is not legal in Britain nowadays to produce capons but the practice still continues in some parts of the world. The term is still used for larger birds weighing about 2.7 - 3.6kg.

 ## CHANTICLEER AND PARTLET

The Adventures of Chanticleer and Partlet are told by the Grimm Brothers in three stories – *How They Went to the Mountains to Eat Nuts, How Chanticleer and Partlet Went to Visit Mr Korbes* and *How Partlet Died and was Buried and How Chanticleer Died of Grief*. In the first story Chanticleer, the cock and Partlet are gathering nuts, the cock has a fight with Duck who is then harnessed to the wagon and made to draw them and their nuts. They arrive exhausted at an inn having picked up Pin and Needle on the way. They promise the Landlord an egg and are allowed to stay but the cock wakes early; they eat the egg, put the egg-shell in the fireplace, leave the Needle stuck in the landlord's chair and the Pin in his hankie and depart – the Duck escapes onto a nearby stream. The Landlord does not have a good morning and says he will never again take in such a pack of ragamuffins (this story is sometimes called *A Pack of Ragamuffins*). In the next story

Chanticleer and Partlet go out in a carriage drawn by six mice. On the way to visit Mr Korbes they pick up a cat, a mill-stone, an egg, a duck and a pin. When they arrive Mr Korbes is out so Chanticleer and Partlet fly up onto a beam, the Cat sits in the fireplace, Duck gets into some water, Pin sticks itself in the pillow, the Mill-stone puts himself over the house-door and the Egg rolls herself in a towel. Suffice it to say Mr Korbes comes to a nasty end when he comes home, running into all sorts of traps and is eventually killed by the Mill-stone. In the final, tragic story Partlet dies from a nut stuck in her throat and after burying her, Chanticleer pines away until he dies as well.

 ## CHANTICLEER AND PERTELOTE

Chanticleer was the cockerel in *The Nun's Priest's Tale* by Chaucer. Chanticleer lives in a widow's farmyard with seven hens, one of which, Pertelote, is his wife. He has a dream about a fox and becomes worried. She assures him that he only suffers from indigestion and chides him for paying heed to a simple dream. Chanticleer is comforted by Pertelote and proceeds to greet a new day. Unfortunately for Chanticleer, his dream becomes a reality. A fox lies in wait and overcomes the cock's instinct to escape by insisting he would love to hear Chanticleer crow just as his amazing father did, with neck outstretched, eyes closed and standing on his tiptoes. When Chanticleer does as he's told, he is promptly snatched. As the fox flees through the forest pursued by the widow and her daughters, the captured Chanticleer suggests that the fox should pause to tell his pursuers to give up their chase. The predator's own pride is now his undoing: as the fox opens his mouth to taunt his pursuers, Chanticleer escapes from his jaws and proceeds to

fly up the nearest tree. The fox tries in vain to tempt the wary cockerel, safe in the tree, but his trickery does not work a second time. This tale is variously retold – one well-known version is *Chanticleer and the Fox* by Barbara Cooney. Chanticleer also features in *Reynard the Fox*.

CHICKEN LICKEN see Hen Tales for Children

 CHICKEN RUN

Chicken Run is a popular animated film made and released in 2000. Ginger, Bunty, Babs and Fowler are chickens trapped on a battery farm and desperately want to escape. If they don't produce any eggs for a week, Mr and Mrs Tweedy will have their heads. When it seems like all their attempts have failed, an American rooster called Rocky drops into the farm. Seeing Rocky flying, Ginger now realises that the only way out is by flying. The chickens must learn to fly before time runs out. The film follows the turbulent romance between Rocky and Ginger, as well as their 'prisoner of war' style escape. It is contested that the film was based on a book called *Escape from Cold Ditch* by Alan Davidson.
See *Escape from Cold Ditch*

CHICKS AND MOTHER HENS
After 20 days for bantams or 21 days for larger fowl, chicks will begin to emerge from their shells. Cheeping will be heard coming from inside the shell about 24 hours before the eggs are due to hatch. While her chicks are hatching, Mother Hen will sit for approximately 48 hours and manage without food or water. She should be left alone for this period. Chicks are nidifugous which

means they can leave their nest soon after hatching so after drying off they will be peeping out from Mother Hen's feathers ready to take their first steps. Chicks do not need anything to eat for at least the first 24 hours because the yolk in their stomachs gives them all the nourishment they need. Chicks should then be fed chick crumbs, which they need to eat for the first six to eight weeks. They can also be given breadcrumbs mixed with chopped up boiled eggs. Mother Hen will be happy to eat the chick feed as she gradually regains her strength after days of semi-starvation. Newly born chicks should be fed every couple of hours. Drinking water is also very important.

In the past people used a specially designed rearing coop in which the hen stays behind bars and cannot disturb the chicks as they feed, drink and run about. This method is unnecessary, unnatural and seems dated in this modern age. It is true that a hen might become quite agitated once she is up and about, scratching the feed all over the place, upsetting the water and scattering her chicks in the process. It is therefore best not to put straw in the coop once the chicks have hatched, as Mother Hen will scratch that up too and may inadvertently kick her chicks and kill or injure them. A simple, small hen house with run attached will be ideal to accommodate hen and chicks. In any case, if they are being moved to new quarters, they should be left until the evening about 24 hours after they have all hatched.

Mother Hen will teach her chicks all they need to know about life and will need a good dust bath a few days after the chicks have hatched. The chicks will quickly learn how to dust bathe themselves at this time as well. After about five weeks the chicks will have grown enough feathers not to need to sleep under Mother Hen any more, although they may still want to. At around eight weeks Mother Hen will slowly lose her attachment to her chicks and return to the flock. She may at this time turn suddenly against the male chicks in particular, and start pecking them. Her maternal instincts disappear and her hormones are now geared for egg laying and she may start laying eggs almost straightaway. The brood of chicks however will tend to stick together once their Mum leaves. Meanwhile, chicks will not become sexually mature until 21 weeks and are now known as pullets.

Plutarch in *Parental Love* writes of Mother Hen and her devotion: 'What of the hens whom we observe each day at home, with what care and assiduity they govern and guard their chicks? Some let down their wings for the chicks to come under; others arch their backs for them to climb upon; there is no part of their bodies with which they do not wish to cherish their chicks if they can, nor do they do this without a joy and willingness which they seem to exhibit by the sound of their voices.'

A story to illustrate how protective a hen is to her chicks:

 Heroism of an Irish Hen - Anon

A contest of rather an unusual nature took place in the house of an innkeeper in Ireland. The parties engaged were a hen of the game

species and a rat of middle size. The hen, in a walk round a spacious room, accompanied by an only chick, the last one left of a large brood, was roused to madness by an attack made by a fierce rat on her helpless little one. The frightened cries of her beloved little chick, while it was being dragged away by the rat, awoke all the mother-love in the bosom of the hen. She flew at the corner whence he had taken her child, seized him by the neck, dragged him about the room, put out one of his eyes, and so tired him by repeated attacks of spur and bill, that in the space of twelve minutes, during which time the conflict lasted, she killed the rat, nimbly turned round in triumph to her frightened nestling, and lovingly sheltered it beneath her protecting wings.

CHIMNEY SWEEP CHICKENS
Farmers and country folk, who did not have access to the young chimney sweeps working in the cities, used chickens and geese to sweep their chimneys. They would tie their feet together and then lower the birds down the chimney and raise them up again; their wings would flap thereby cleaning the chimney. Apparently in France farmers still use this method!

CHINESE YEAR OF THE ROOSTER
The rooster is the 10th symbolic animal in the 12 year Chinese Zodiac cycle. It was the year of the Wood Rooster back in 2005; it will be the year of the Fire Rooster in 2017. Those born in the year of the rooster are said to be sociable, shrewd, very accomplished, outspoken, boastful, courageous, practical but also dreamers, to name just a few of the personality traits believed to belong to cockerels.

 **CLARA CLUCK**

Clara Cluck is a Disney character appearing in Mickey Mouse cartoons – she made her first appearance in *Orphan's Benefit* in 1934.

CLOACA

The cloaca is the posterior opening that serves as the only opening for the intestinal, reproductive and urinary tracts in chickens. The word comes from the Latin and means sewer.

See also Vent

CLOACAL KISS

This is the name given to the cockerel's mating with a hen. He pounces on her back, grabbing the top of her head with his beak and sprays his sperm (he does not have a penis). The hen wiggles until it transfers into her cloaca from his – this is all done in a few seconds, no emotion involved particularly as one cockerel may have a number of hens to see to each day!

CLUCKING

Scientists used to think that only a few mammals could understand the meanings of different calls. Now research has shown that chickens have a more advanced use and understanding of language than scientists expected. The German scientist Dr Baeumer studied their language and made a list of 30 different calls. These varied from the cries of chicks separated from their mother (pieep-pieep-pieep) and their terror trills, a high pitched trr-tr to the frightened cackles of hens and cockerels when they first see danger. After

danger passes, the cackling becomes full-throated, rhythmical and triumphant. Hens cackle when they have laid an egg (this might mean 'I've done well, I've laid an egg' or might just be a cackling to regain contact with rest of the flock). Hens make screams of distress; they have battle cries and calls for privacy. Hens lead their chicks to food with a gentle 'tuck, tuck, tuck' and cockerels entice pretty young hens with soft cooing. Hens make contented, almost purring noises when given edible treats or when digging is going on and worms emerge. Chicken behaviour is not too different from human behaviour (competing for women, food and the best nesting places) nor is the chicken language!

CLUTCH

A clutch is the term used for all the eggs a hen lays in succession before she stops and wants to sit on them. If the eggs have been taken away on a regular basis, she may take a few days off before starting to lay another clutch.

A Clutch or Chattering of chicks is also the collective name for a group of chicks.

COCCIDIOSIS AND COCCODISIATS

This disease is caused by the Coccidia – a protozoan parasite – which affects the digestive tract. Symptoms will include listlessness with head sunk into the neck, white diarrhoea and sometimes blood in the droppings. Coccidiosis spreads through the droppings and thrives in chicken manure. Proleth in the drinking water can be used to treat the disease. Preventatives, known as Coccodisiats are added to chick crumbs.

COCHIN

The Cochin originally came from China in the 1850s where it was known as the Shanghai. Cochins brought on boats from the port of Canton in southern China were presented to the young Queen Victoria.

They were first exhibited at the Birmingham Show in 1850 – Lewis Wright (*Illustrated Book of Poultry*) writes: 'Every visitor went home to tell of these new wonderful fowl, which were as big as ostriches, and roared like lions, while as gentle as lambs; which could be kept anywhere, even in a garret …' Originally with clean legs the Cochin became very popular owing to its size and laying powers. However exhibition breeders turned the Cochin into a 'bag of feathers' and it eventually lost its good name. Now similar to the Brahma with feathered legs and feet, it is a heavy soft-feathered breed and lays tinted eggs. There are no miniatures of this bird but Pekin bantams are a similar small version.

See also Victoria, Queen

COCK, ORIGIN OF THE WORD

Some suppose that 'cock' is an onomatopoeic word imitating the male fowl's call, a shortening of cock-a-doodle-doo. In many languages the word cock is similar: in Latin it was cucurio (I crow) and the medieval Latin word was coccus; in Sanskrit kukkuta; in German kuchlein; the old English word was kok and the Middle

44

English word was cok. What is certain is that in many cultures the word for the male chicken is the same as for the word penis – in Greece and in Rome the sexuality of the cock was all-important – the extreme erectness of the cock, straining forward and upward suggested the erect penis and in Greek sculptures the cock was often depicted with the head and neck as a phallus – these statues could be said to be celebrating life force. The word 'cock' for something that sticks up and is cylindrical was also thought to be derived from stopcock. The Americans adopted the word Rooster in the 1800s, presumably because of the association with penis – the Victorians certainly deemed the word cock vulgar; Louisa May Alcott, the authoress of *Little Women*, originally had the surname Allcock but her father changed it to Alcott. In this country nowadays we tend to use the word cockerel although this was originally only used for a young male bird.

COCK-A-DOODLE-DOO, THE CROWING OF THE NOBLE COCK, BENEVANTANO by Herman Melville (1853)

This is an unusual short story by the author of Moby Dick: the narrator is despairing about himself and his world but upon hearing the noble cock crow he overflows with self-reliance and a sense of security. He goes after the cock which belongs to a poor, starving family, whose plight is glorified by the magnificent crowing of the majestic bird. The narrator witnesses the death of the family while the cock still crows but in the midst of his crowing he drops dead. The cock symbolises the impractical idealist who says everything is wonderful in the very face of poverty and death.

45

COCK AND BULL STORY

This is a term we use for a long, rambling, incredible story. Its origins are obscure. The phrase is used most notably in Laurence Sterne's *Tristam Shandy* – the last words of the book are 'Lord! Said my mother what is all this story about – a cock and a bull, said Yorick – and one of the best of its kind, I ever heard' and this is how the term may have originated in 1760. However other suggestions for its origin are: old fables which have magical animals talking to one another and someone who hated listening to such tales may have dubbed them as Cock and Bull; the French phrase 'coq-al'ane' meant literally 'cock to donkey' and became cockalane in Scots meaning a rambling, disconnected story. In Stony Stratford the London coach changed horses at The Bull and the Birmingham coach across the road at The Cock Inn – the passengers from the two coaches would swap news whilst waiting, hence Cock and Bull Stories.

COCKADE

Originally this was a plume of cockerels' feathers with which the Croats in the service of the French in the 17th Century adorned their caps. Now it is a rosette worn in the hat as the badge of an office or party.

COCK-A-HOOP

Cock-a-hoop, meaning in great spirits, has two possible origins – the most plausible is that it is a transliteration of the French phrase 'coq a huppe,' meaning a rooster displaying its crest (huppe) in a pose of proud defiance. Thus, 'cock-a-hoop' would liken someone to a boastful and aggressive rooster. The other theory is that the

cock refers to the tap on a keg of ale and so to set the cock on the hoop means simply to turn on the tap.

COCK-A-LEEKIE
This is a Scottish soup of chicken and leeks.

COCKALORUM
A bantam or small cockerel but also cockalorum is a term for a self-important, little man.

 **COCKATRICE**

The cockatrice is similar to the basilisk, resembling a large cockerel with feet and a lizard-like tail. The cockatrice was believed to be the product of a seven-year-old cockerel's egg, laid during a full moon and then hatched for nine years by a serpent or toad. There were only a few ways to protect oneself against a cockatrice. One was to carry a mirror and turn the creature's gaze back on it, causing it to die instantly. Another was to keep either a weasel or a cockerel nearby. The weasel was said to be the mortal enemy of the cockatrice, while the crowing of the cockerel would also cause the cockatrice to die instantly.

In 1474 in Basle, a cockerel was thought to have laid an egg that would hatch a cockatrice. He was tried and convicted of sorcery, then burnt at the stake along with the egg. In 1538, a cockatrice was reputed to have hatched in the cellars of Wherwell Abbey in Hampshire and to have devoured several people before being destroyed. A weathercock was made in its image and placed on the church spire as a warning to the Devil.

See also Basilisk

COCKERELS

Today the cockerel is regarded as a nuisance by many because of his crowing and is kept principally for breeding and showing. In contrast to the Ancient Greeks and Romans he was hugely important with many virtues and several uses; he was a thing of beauty and a symbol of sex, the sun, resurrection, bravery, divine power and much admired for his martial values. He was:

a) The herald of dawn and the timekeeper – soldiers changed their watch by the cock crowing and he awoke people to go to work.

b) The foreteller of the future and forecaster of the weather.

c) A symbol of sex and used as a love gift by older men to young boys they wanted to seduce.

d) An entertainer as a fighting cock.

e) A symbol of bravery and therefore an attribute of Ares and Hercules – the Greeks believed that even lions were afraid of cocks – he was tied to soldiers' chariots and used as guard, watchman, clock and a symbol of the martial spirit.

f) Used as a sacrifice to the Gods (he was sacred to Aesculapius, God of Healing and Medicine who had the power to raise the dead to life).

g) A symbol of resurrection (crowing at dawn which was the resurrection of night into day).

h) His body was used for medicinal purposes (testicles were fed to the weak for strength and blood was drunk for various ailments).

Aldrovandi (see separate entry) describes the cock: 'He … is for us the example of the best and truest father of a family. For he not only presents himself as a vigilant guardian of his little ones and in the morning invites us to our daily labour; but he sallies forth as the first, not only with his crowing, by which he shows what must

be done, but he sweeps everything, explores and spies out everything. When the cock has found some food he calls both hens and chicks together to eat it while he stands like a father and host at a banquet … Meanwhile he scurries about to find something nearby and when he has found it, he calls his family again in a loud voice. They run to the spot. He stretches himself up, looks around for any danger that may be near, runs about the entire poultry yard, here and there plucking up a grain or two for himself without ceasing to invite the others to follow him … that he fights for his dear wives and little pledges to fortune against serpents, kites, weasels, and other characteristics add … the fact that he fights for his dear wives and beasts of the sort and invites us to a similar combat whenever the occasion presents itself,' and Aldrovandi notes, 'when the hen dies, he takes over her duties, sitting on the eggs ...'

A cockerel is not needed for hens to lay eggs but will be needed for fertile eggs in order to hatch chicks. Cockerels can disturb neighbours by crowing in the night and at dawn but do have some advantages. They can prove surprisingly thoughtful when looking after the hens on their patch, often calling them over to enjoy tasty morsels.

They usually do most of their mating between March and October. Young fertile cockerels generally have a red tinge showing on their legs. A cockerel will approach a hen and stand erect in front of her with his neck feathers ruffled. He will then dance around her with the wing nearest her spread downwards. The hen, if a submissive one, will duck down and allow him to mount her. He will use his wings to maintain his balance and grip her by the nape of her neck while he mates (hens may lose some feathers on top of their heads as a result). The cockerel may also be quite cunning,

luring his hens over by calling them to food and then jumping on them! The problems with mating occur with the high-ranking hens who will often object to mating by flying off and refusing to let the cock near them.

Research has been carried out on cockerels and their reproductive abilities. Cockerels will apparently produce more sperm if a new hen comes on the scene. They will also devote more sperm to their first mating with a new hen. They may also increase the sperm if rival cockerels are around. An attractive hen with a large comb will receive more sperm than a less attractive female. These large-combed hens will also tend to be reproductively superior, producing more eggs with bigger yolks.

The main problem when rearing chicks is getting rid of the cockerels. An average of 60% of chicks turn out to be male and keeping too many cockerels means they will fight as they are territorial. An older cockerel can usually remain dominant if one or two young cockerels are being allowed to grow up on his patch but if an entirely new cockerel is introduced they will fight, perhaps fatally. Pure breed cockerels can often be sold or given away. Otherwise they must be killed.

To wring the neck it must be gripped firmly while the bird is held by its feet. Pull down on the neck, and then quickly bend it upwards until the neck snaps. Make the movement in one strong, fluid motion. After the chicken's neck snaps, the wings will start to flap as a last reflex. In the old days people would then drop the chicken and let it run around before dying. Hence the term: 'run around like headless chickens'. A trip to an obliging vet is another option.

See also Crowing

 COCKEREL TALES

The cockerel has inspired many stories over the years and has been written about down the centuries.

From Shakespeare's Hamlet, Act 1, Scene 1
Horatio
And then it started like a guilty thing
Upon a fearful summons. I have heard,
The cock, that is the trumpet to the morn,
Doth with his lofty and shrill-sounding throat
Awake the god of day; and, at his warning,
Whether in sea or fire, in earth or air,
The extravagant and erring spirit hies
To his confine: and of the truth herein
This present object made probation.

Marcellus
It faded on the crowing of the cock.
Some say that ever 'gainst that season comes
Wherein our Saviour's birth is celebrated,
The bird of dawning singeth all night long:
And then, they say, no spirit dares stir abroad;
The nights are wholesome; then no planets strike,
No fairy takes, nor witch hath power to charm,
So hallow'd and so gracious is the time.

Shakespeare's Richard III Act V, Scene 3
The early village cock
Hath twice done salutation to the morn.

Milton's Allegro

While the cock with lively din
Scatters the rear of darkness thin
And to the stack of the barn door
Stoutly struts his dames before.

A Story from India

The demon wished to wed Goddess Kamakhya. He threatened to destroy everything if she refused him. She gave him one condition, asking him to build a temple overnight and if he managed that she would be his in the morning. The demon got to work and was just finishing the temple well before dawn. Seeing that her hope that he would fail hadn't materialised, she asked her trusted cockerel to crow. Just as the last bricks were about to be laid, the cock crowed, declaring the arrival of dawn. The temple was thus left incomplete and the Goddess was spared the humiliation of marrying a demon. The temple is now one of the most sacred pilgrimage sites, located in Guwahati, Assam.

An Extract from The Cock who Taught his Master – Legends of Animals Far and Near by Rose Yeatman Woolf

This is a politically incorrect tale about a master taming his wife with the help of advice from his cockerel.

'Before long Giovanni made the discovery that he had married a shrew who made his life a burden to him … he let her have her way in everything and she soon became master of the household. He escaped by spending much time out-of-doors, caring for the animals on the farm whose gratitude gave him much satisfaction. None suspected his secret and neighbours ascribed the judgment he displayed in sowing and reaping at the most favourable moment

to good luck, rather than the weather-lore of the birds, nor could they guess that his cleverness in finding hidden eggs was due to the indiscreet clucking of the hens. Giovanni was sitting by the fire one wet evening when the cat came into the room and made an insulting remark to Fidelio who was stretched at his master's feet. 'Peace,' growled the dog. 'What is the use of scolding all day. You are just as bad as our mistress. I am tired to the death of the pair of you.' This remark so tickled Giovanni's humour that he burst into a loud laugh which continued until the tears ran down his cheeks. 'What are you laughing at?' inquired his wife …

'Can't a man laugh if he wants to?' Giovanni retorted.

'Not without a cause,' said his wife with rising anger. 'Now answer me without further shilly-shally.'

'Pray, don't insist upon my telling you for if I did I should give away a secret upon the keeping of which my life depends,' was the imprudent reply. The shrew's curiosity being now thoroughly aroused she gave her husband no peace in her persistence to discover the secret. Worn out at last by her nagging, Giovanni cried to his wife: 'You make my life so miserable that I may as well tell you my secret and die.' So saying he went to the carpenter's where he ordered a coffin … he had it placed outside the door, stretched himself inside it, and took what he thought to be a farewell look at the farm. Fidelio sat beside the coffin and howled. A cock strutting by observing a fat worm close to the coffin ran forward and picked it up greedily. The dog stopped howling and regarded the cock with disgust. 'Wretched bird,' he growled, 'how can you be so unfeeling as to think of food when our beloved master is about to die?'

'Cock-a-doodle-do,' laughed the cock. 'I have no respect for such a foolish fellow. He is better dead for he has not the wit to rule

one wife, whereas I exact obedience from a dozen. If any one of my women-folk dares question my wishes, I peck her till she thinks better of it; that is the way for a man to manage his household.'

When Giovanni heard these words he jumped from the coffin and running to the stable returned with a whip. 'Wife,' shouted he, 'come here and you shall learn my secret in a way you little expect.'

The woman observing his angry face and the flourishing whip ran indoors and shouted that she had lost all desire to hear his secret. Giovanni stored his whip in the corner of the room and when his wife lost her temper he had only to flourish this weapon to bring her back to reason. Thus was the shrew tamed and Giovanni vowed that he would never forget the lesson he had learnt from the cock who knew how to be master of his household.'

The Golden Cockerel

This was a fable written by Pushkin and became a Russian Opera by Rimsky-Korsakov. A golden cockerel is given by a sorcerer to Tsar Dadon; in return for this favour he will be granted his first wish whatever it may be. The golden cockerel is placed on the top of the spire and warns the Tsar of imminent peril from enemies by crowing and turning to face the direction of the danger. After years of peace the cockerel crows and the Tsar sends an army with his first son; the cockerel crows again and another army is sent with his second son; the cockerel crows again and the Tsar sets off with a third army. His sons are dead but he meets the beautiful Princess Shamakhan and brings her home – as he enters the city the sorcerer asks for his wish to be granted – he would like the princess. The Tsar refuses and the cockerel swoops down and kills him whilst the Princess vanishes into thin air.

Cocksure Women and Hensure Men – An Essay by DH Lawrence 1920

It is quite amusing to see the two kinds of sureness in chickens. The cockerel is, naturally, cocksure. He crows because he is certain it is day. Then the hen peeps out from under her wing. He marches to the door of the hen house and pokes out his head assertively: Ah-ha! daylight! Just as I said! And he majestically steps down the chicken ladder towards terra firma, knowing that the hens will step cautiously after him, drawn by his confidence ... He crows again ... It is indisputable, and the hens accept it entirely. He marches towards the house. From the house a person ought to appear, scattering corn. Why does the person not appear? The cock will see to it. He is cocksure. He gives a loud crow in the doorway and the person appears. The hens are suitably impressed, but immediately devote all their henny consciousness to the scattered corn, pecking absorbedly, while the cock runs and fusses, cocksure that he is responsible for it all. So the day goes on. The cock finds a tit-bit, and loudly calls the hens. They scuffle up in henny surety, and gobble the tit-bit. But when they find a juicy morsel for themselves, they devour it in silence, hensure. Unless, of course, there are little chicks, when they most anxiously call the brood. But in her own dim surety, the hen is really much surer than the cock, in a different way.

She marches off to lay her egg, she secures obstinately the nest she wants, she lays her egg at last, then steps forth again with prancing confidence, and gives that most assured of all sounds, the hensure cackle of a bird who has laid her egg. The cock, who is never so sure about anything as the hen is about the egg she has laid, immediately starts to cackle like the female. He is pining to be hensure, for hensure is so much surer than cocksure.

Nevertheless, cocksure is boss. When the hawk appears in the sky, loud are the cockerel's calls of alarm. Then the hens scuffle under the veranda, the cock ruffles his feathers on guard. The hens are numb with fear, they say: Alas, there is no health in us! How wonderful to be a cock so bold! ... But their very numbness is hensurety. Just as the cock can cackle, however, as if he had laid the egg, so can the hen bird crow. She can more or less assume his cocksureness. And yet she is never so easy, cocksure, as she used to be when she was hensure. Cocksure, she is cocksure, but uneasy. Hensure, she trembles, but is easy. It seems to me just the same in the vast human farmyard. Only nowadays all the cocks are cackling and pretending to lay eggs, and all the hens are crowing and pretending to call the sun out of bed.

If women today are cocksure, men are hensure. Men are timid, tremulous, rather soft and submissive, easy in their very henlike tremulousness. They only want to be spoken to gently. So the women step forth with a good loud cock-a-doodle-doo. The tragedy about cocksure women is that they are more cocky, in their assurance, than the cock himself. They never realise that when the cock gives his loud crow in the morning, he listens acutely afterwards, to hear if some other wretch of a cock dare crow defiance, challenge ... But alas, when the hen crows, she listens for no defiance or challenge. When she says cock-a-doodle-doo, then it is unanswerable. The cock listens for an answer, alert. But the hen knows she is unanswerable. Cock-a-doodle-doo and there it is, take it or leave it! And it is this that makes the cocksureness of women so dangerous … So we have the tragedy of cocksure women. They find, so often, that instead of having laid an egg they have laid a vote, or an empty ink-bottle, or some other absolutely unhatchable object, which means nothing to them …

See also *The Escaped Cock*

The Crowing of Cocks from Impressions and Comments by Havelock Ellis

Now that I sleep lightly at night, since I rest all day, I hear, on this outskirts of the Kentish town, now and again in the hour following midnight and again in the early dawn when all birds else are still silent, the crowing of cocks. To me there is something pleasant and reassuring in this sound. I share not at all the feeling of those who hear it with horror. I am even tempted to think they suffer from an evil conscience. For the cock is traditionally associated in the Christian world with the voice of conscience and the violation of it that brings remorse. Peter might well go out and weep bitterly a certain night when the cock crew. For all his life after there could be no natural sound so keen and so poignant as the crowing cock and I can well understand how at last he sought refuge from it in the largest city in the world and became, according to legend Bishop of Rome. But for my own part I experience no such feeling. I suppose that the Domestic Fowl was the first bird enslaved by Man and perhaps the first Oriental creature artificially introduced into our part of the globe. Yet after millenniums of domestication the Red Jungle Fowl of south-eastern Asia – however degenerate he may have become and even with, they say, the final languid note added to his cry – remains almost as proud and independent as our hieratic Egyptian cat. It is even like an exotic in nature and though I have never heard it in its Asiatic home it scarcely seems to me it can ever have fitted into the natural chorus. There is a disdainful aristocratic isolation about this bird which chooses earth's most silent moments to assert itself and trample down the phenomenal aspects of nature in order to proclaim the triumph of some higher order. So it has never been idealised by those who love nature –

no Wordsworth has written a sentimental ode to the cock – but rather by those who have sought the symbol of vigilance of the moral affirmation of the Universe of the call to man to be awake and watchful. Yet there is in that call the note of knowledge and assurance. At the hour when human vitality is at its lowest ebb and despair nearest to hand then it is that the watchman of the earth raises his voice and the cock crows: All is well with the world.
See also Crowing

COCKFIGHTING

Cockfighting is an ancient sport going back thousands of years; it's the oldest pleasure sport known to man and was being practised long before poultry was bred for meat and eggs. It was not however practised by primitive tribes for whom cocks were sacred. Game cocks were used for fighting, descended from the Red Jungle Fowl of India and the Grey Jungle Fowl of Malaya. Cockfighting was prevalent in Ancient Greece, first mentioned in the 4th Century BC and known to have been practised in south east Asia and India. Themistocles (527 – 462BC) made cockfighting a national sport in Greece and organised cockfights in Athens to inspire his troops.

Many of the ancient writers wrote on the subject and the Romans adopted the sport enthusiastically. Columella wrote in the 1st Century AD that devotees often spent the whole of their patrimony in betting at the pitside. The Phoenicians may well have brought cockfighting to Britain. When Caesar arrived in 55AD he reported that the Britons were already keeping birds for pleasure and amusement. It was however opposed by the Christian church. William Fitz-Stephen speaks of it in the time of Henry II as a sport for schoolboys. Cockfighting gave the ordinary people a chance to bet and to be spectators.

Breeding the cockerels was an important part of the sport as was feeding and training them. To fight, the cockerels had their combs and wattles cut or dubbed so that their opponents had nothing to grip. Their feathers, wings and tails were also trimmed or cut out to make them more mobile and the natural spurs were cut short so that artificial spurs or heels could be fitted. These spurs, made of silver or steel, sometimes had blades as well.

Cockspur Street in London was so called because the spurs were made there. Fighting cocks had to be of the same weight. The two cocks fought in a cockpit which was usually circular with a padded barrier encircling it. The 'setters-on' placed the cocks facing each other and the cocks fought until one died or refused to continue fighting. Single fights formed part of a 'main' which was an agreed odd number of fights. The cock winning the most fights was the victor. There were two variations – the battle royal which was a free-for-all between a number of cocks released in the pit at the same time. The Welsh main was a knock out competition for eight or 16 cockerels. There were two other sports involving cockerels that were also practised to a lesser degree: 'Throwing at Cocks' and 'Thrashing at Cocks' (see Cock Throwing). Cockfighting started to decline in popularity as horse-racing took over in the

late 1700s. In Britain, as in most of the western world, cockfighting was made illegal in 1849 under Queen Victoria's rule. One exception was the custom that allowed cockfighting on Shrove Tuesday at boarding schools – young boys would pay their masters a cock fee (called cock-penny) and bring in their game cocks; cockfighting would ensue – the pupil whose cock survived was spared any punishments during Lent and the master in charge would receive all the dead cocks.

Cockfighting is still practised illegally in countries where it was banned and in a number of Asian countries, the Philippines and Borneo, for example this bloody sport is still as popular as ever, and is seen as part of the culture.

There are several expressions in the English language that stem from cockfighting. 'Pitted against' was used by cockers when two cocks were placed in the pit. The wings and tail were 'cut out' as already mentioned and when we say 'he was not cut out for the job' we use this old cocking term. The cutting of the feathers was called 'dressing the cocks' – we use this expression when we say 'dressed to kill'. Cocky and cocksure are also taken from the sport.

COCK THROWING

Cock throwing, also known as cock-shying or whipping the cock was a blood sport practised in England in the 1600s and 1700s. A cockerel was tied to a post and people took turns in throwing coksteles, which were special weighted sticks, from a distance of about 10 metres, at the target. Competitors had to catch the felled cockerel before he stood up again. The prize was a cockerel for dinner. A variation on cock throwing was 'Thrashing at Cocks' in

which a cockerel was put in a pit and struck at by a blindfolded person – if the cock was killed it was the prize for dinner.

COCKPITS

Henry VIII enjoyed cockfighting and built a royal cockpit at Whitehall. Most towns across Britain ended up with a cockpit. The cockpit in Birdcage Walk in London was depicted by Hogarth. The oldest open-air pit was the Gwenap Pit in Devon. The late 18th Century brick-built cockpit at Welshpool in Powys was restored in 1978 and is the only cockpit in Wales still in its original location. It could hold 150 spectators; there is also a thatched cockpit in Denbigh.

The Denbigh cockpit

COCK'S EGG

This is the term used for a very small egg often laid at the end of the season or at the end of a clutch – sometimes thought of as the 'runt' of the clutch. It can also be called a witch's egg. It doesn't usually have any yolk in it.

COCKSFOOT

Cocksfoot is a tufted perennial grass whose flowerhead has three or more compact spikes reminiscent of a cock's foot.

COCKSTRIDE

This is a northern expression for a very small distance. It was used in connection with the increase in daylight in early January – 'days are getting a cockstride longer'.

COCKTAIL

Among the various stories as to the origin of this name for a mixture of alcoholic drinks the most attractive is that it was drunk as a toast in the days of cockfighting to the cock that had the most tail feathers left after a battle!

COLOURS

Hens and cockerels come in a mind boggling array of colours with many variations in the breeds. Males and females of one breed often exhibit different colours and feather markings within colours can also vary. Black, white, brown, buff, salmon, wheaten and red are self-explanatory. Lavender is light grey and blue is also grey but often with a darker grey lacing. Cuckoo is where the feathers have bands of light and dark grey or lemon cuckoo is bands of white and buff. Some of the names used are complicated by the fact that they combine colour and markings on the bird's plumage. Partridge is further complicated because it is sexually dimorphic (males are completely different in appearance to the females) – in Partridge Wyandottes for example males are a traditional black-red whilst the females are pencilled with black on a golden yellow; in Welsummers males are black-red but females are brown with golden brown on the neck and feathers stippled with black specks. Other complicated colours include Millefleur – ground colour is mahogany and each feather has a crescent-

shaped bar of black with a V white spangle; Red Pyle – is a mixture of chestnut red, white and a deeper red in the male with the female having a white basic colour with a golden head and tinges of salmon over the rest of her body (there is also a Lemon Pyle version); Columbian – basic colour is white with black lacing in the neck and black tail feathers; the reverse of this is silver-necked or Birchen where basic colour is black with white lacing on the neck (the tail remains black); Porcelaine is where the feathers are three-coloured – ground colour is brown but the tips of feathers have a black spot or spangle with a speck of white in the middle (blue Porcelaine and silver Porcelaine have ground colours of grey and white respectively), the Quail colour can come in a host of different variants from blue, silver, and lavender and are reminiscent of quail.

See also Feathers

COMBS

Combs can vary greatly in size and shape between breeds. The single comb is probably the most common but can vary in size and is called a folded single or semi-erect single if it flops over. Rose and pea combs are also fairly popular; the rose comb is flat on top but is covered with small points rather like a hairbrush. A pea comb is a triple comb with three single combs, distinctly divided but joined at the ends. There are some very unusual combs such as the horn, the cup, the leaf, the mulberry and the strawberry (also called walnut). The Sultan breed has a horn comb. The Sicilian Buttercup has a cup comb. The leaf comb can be seen on a Houdan. The mulberry comb is seen on a Silkie.

1. Single (cock)
2. Single (hen)
3. Single (small)
4. Single (high)
5. Undeveloped
6. Pea (triple)
7. Flat rose
8. Large rose
9. Curved rose
10. Leaf
11. Wide horn
12. Horn

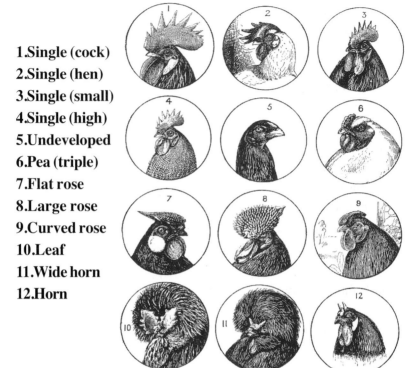

CORKY

Corky the Cockerel was the subject of one of the most celebrated noise disputes ending in court. Corky crowed so loudly at 5am that a noise abatement order was slapped on his owner after a complaint from neighbours in the hamlet of Stoke, near Hartland in North Devon. The case was dealt with in the county court, where the judge ruled that the owner had a duty to keep Corky silent between midnight and 7am. This happened back in 1994.

See Crowing, George, Victoire

COXCOMB

A coxcomb is a strip of red cloth which is toothed like a cock's comb and which professional jesters would wear. Coxcomb is also another word for a fop or dandy.

CREST

The crest is a tuft of feathers on the head also sometimes known as the topknot. In Old English Game it is known as the Tassel. Araucanas have small crests; Silkies have slightly larger crests; Polands have huge crests which come down over their eyes, often obscuring their view.

CROCK EGGS

These are fake eggs and can be china, plastic or rubber. They are also known as pot or china eggs and are designed to be put in the nest box to encourage hens to start laying or, if already laying, to lay in the right place. The ancients realised the importance of using a fake egg and theirs were made of marble or stone. We get the term 'nest-egg' from this use of crock eggs – if a person has saved a little money, why not use this as an inducement to save more.

CROP AND CROP BOUND

The crop is situated at the front of the chicken below the neck. Hens and cockerels have no teeth so food picked up by the beak is carried into the gullet by the tongue and from there goes into the crop. The crop is like a food store and can be quite large by the end of the day. Here grain etc. is softened by saliva coming from glands in the mouth. Food passes from the crop into the stomach where gastric juices are released. It is then transferred to the gizzard where it is ground up. The crop will be empty by morning.

If a hen is crop bound or has an impacted crop it will feel hard and even hang down heavily. If the hen is picked up, a hard ball of food which has accumulated will be felt – often this is a twisted ball of grass which is then too large to pass down. A lubricant such as a little olive oil can be poured down her throat – this is easiest done with a syringe and if the crop is then gently massaged, the food

should soften and pass through. Liquid paraffin can be used as an alternative to olive oil (olive oil can be bad for the chicken's liver) – liquid paraffin does not go through the liver but passes out with the droppings. Alternatively the hen can be given a drink of warm water, then turned upside down and the crop gently massaged to try and release the blockage. The hen can be fed some soft food in the interim. If the impaction does not clear then the best option is to consult a vet – he may make a small incision in her breast and be able to remove the blockage.

CROWING

The cockerel's crowing at dawn was deemed very important by the ancients. Soldiers changed watch timed by the cock's crowing. The Roman writer, Pliny claimed that 'sluggish men would never rise from their beds with the exhortations of the crested bird.' The Romans divided the night into parts – midnight - 3am was called gallicinium – the time when cocks begin to crow. The next was conticinium when they stopped crowing and last was diluculum – dawn – when the cock crows a second time.

Cocks were valued as weather forecasters, predicting rain with their raucous crowing and flapping of wings. It was also believed that when the cock crowed at dawn all ghosts and evil spirits would return to the underworld.

Cock crowing competitions used to take place in the US in the early 1900s as well as across Europe and Russia where the Yurlov Crower (see separate entry) was bred specifically for competitions. In these competitions a time-keeper would note down the duration of each contestant's crow and the number of crows in a given length of time, usually up to 30 minutes. An anonymous writer

described a crowing competition in the US in 1901: 'the mode of operation is to place the cages containing the roosters in a long row and then one bird will generally set the others crowing. A marker for each bird, appointed by the organiser of the show, has as his duty to note carefully the number of crows made by his bird. Each competitor puts up one dollar and the winner takes all.'

In Germany there is a breed called Bergse Kraaier which has a reputation for having the longest and loudest crow. Turkey has also produced birds with long crows some lasting for 30 seconds, apparently. In the US today there are still cock crowing competitions where the winner is the bird that crows the most in 30 minutes.

In the last few years cock crowing has proved a sensitive issue between chicken keepers and their neighbours – several cases have been either brought to court or settled by the Local Council. If complaints are received, the Council are obliged to investigate. Environmental Services Officers will consider: the source of noise, environment of the noise, duration of crowing, time of day and how often the cockerel crows. Practical measures will be suggested such as moving the said cockerel as far away from neighbouring properties as possible; keeping the housing as dark as possible and even lowering the ceiling so that the cockerel is prevented from throwing his head back to crow. Competition between other cockerels in the area can also be a problem.

Stories abound in local papers of cases involving crowing cockerels and Councils issuing Noise Abatement Notices. Four cockerels on a farm in Radlett, Hertfordshire are to be seized by the Council and re-homed if nothing is done to quieten them. A cockerel, Basil, was saved and re-homed on a farm in Bamburgh, Northumberland after a campaign to save him on the social-

networking site, Facebook, who now lives with his favourite hen, Bonnet. Bruce the cockerel has also had to be re-homed after one neighbour complained to a farmer in Widnes.

People are always searching for ways to silence crowing. In the US cockerels can be taken to the vet and have their vocal chords removed; in Britain this is not allowed. Making a hen house sound proof is impossible because birds must have ventilation. One method that has been used is to put a bar across the roof loosely so that it swings when the cockerel's head touches it, as he throws his head back. But a canny cockerel would just jump down from his perch to crow standing on the floor. In Los Angeles the City Council has voted to limit the number of roosters to one per household – this will help control cockfighting and combat concerns over noise pollution. Residents who already have more than one cockerel can apply for a permit at a cost of $50 to keep an additional two cockerels but they cannot be replaced after their deaths.

See also Cockerels, Corky, George, Victoire

CROWING HENS

Some hens are known to develop cock-like characteristics and start crowing. This is usually caused by hormonal changes which may be the result of an infected ovary. The infection will often clear up with antibiotics, or it may clear of its own accord. The hormonal change means that the testosterone levels will soar so that, apart from the crowing, the hen may develop an enlarged comb, spurs and male plumage after a moult. She may also try to mount other hens. If the cause is an infected ovary, and it clears up, she will probably revert to her usual state. A dominant hen living in a group with no resident cockerel, may also start crowing as a sign of her authority.

D

DAY-OLD CHICKS

Day-old chicks can be bought from breeders. They will need to be kept in a brooder for four to six weeks or they can be mothered by a broody hen but need to be introduced within 24 hours of her own brood being hatched. A Silkie hen, though, should adopt chicks even a few days after her own are hatched.

DEFRA

DEFRA stands for Department of the Environment, Food and Rural Affairs. Anyone with a flock of hens exceeding 50 in number must register with DEFRA.

DERBYSHIRE REDCAP

The redcap is similar in appearance to the Old English Pheasant Fowl but has red earlobes rather than white and an unusually large rose comb covered in evenly sized spikes. The Derbyshire Redcap is a light, soft-feathered breed and is red-spangled in colour. The breed is a reasonable layer of tinted or white eggs. There is also a rare bantam version.

DIOMEDE

Diomede was the French cockerel and rugby mascot who was sent back home to Brisbane in Australia after suffering from depression in the 2003 World Cup. The fed-up fowl was rumbled, by the Fijians before France had even played a match, as not being a genuine French bird, and so the strain of his double life caught up with him. Despite the allegations about his Australian identity, Diomede had bravely run along the touchline at all France's training sessions.

DOMESTIC FOWL TRUST

Based near Evesham in Worcestershire the Trust is a rare breed farm park which now incorporates a Visitor Centre and Museum designed to increase the public awareness of poultry and the history of domestic fowl. There are 20 acres filled with runs for a vast range of poultry including turkeys, ducks, geese, guinea fowl and pheasants as well as many breeds of chickens. There is a large shop selling a wide range of poultry related items including housing and birds, and food is served in the Speckled Hen tea room.

DOMINIQUE

The Dominique is one of the oldest American breeds (available as large fowl and bantams) with a distinctive slate colouring formed by irregular light and dark barring of black and white in the feathers. Hens lay brown eggs. There are only a handful of Dominique breeders in Britain.

DORKING

It is thought that the Dorking is one of the oldest domesticated fowl, possibly introduced into Britain by the Romans; a similar bird

with five toes was described by Pliny, the Roman writer, in his *Natural History*. The five toes are a distinctive feature of the bird which originated in Dorking and the surrounding area in Surrey and is a heavy, soft-feathered breed laying tinted eggs. In the female, the single comb flops over to one side. Dorkings are large but have short legs. Bantam versions are also available.

Colours vary from cuckoo to red, silver grey and white. This breed is on the Rare Breeds Survival Trust list. However the breed has been used in autosexing to produce the Dorbar. Since February 2007 a 3 metre high silver statue of the cockerel has stood on Deepdene roundabout at the eastern approach to Dorking, ensuring that travellers are acquainted with the town and at least a little part of its history. It has become known as the Deepdene Dorking.

A symbol of the Dorking cockerel can be seen on the roadside approaches to Dorking. Dorking hens feature in Edward Lear's nonsense song, *The Courtship of the Yonghy-Bonghy-Bo*: 'Once, among the Bong-trees walking/Where the early pumpkins blow/ To a little heap of stones/Came the Yonghy-Bonghy-Bo/There he heard a Lady talking/To some milk-white Hens of Dorking/'Tis the Lady Jingly Jones!/On that little heap of stones/Sits the Lady Jingly Jones!/Said the Yonghy-Bonghy-Bo,/Said the Yonghy-Bonghy-Bo.'

DRINKING

Fresh water needs to be available to chickens at all times. There are a number of different sized drinkers on the market made of either plastic or galvanized metal. Plastic drinkers are preferable in winter when the water freezes – the ice can be removed easily. Galvanized drinkers need hot water to unfreeze the water inside them. However, they are more durable but also more expensive. Drinkers can become dirty with green algae. A few drops of cider vinegar in the water can prevent the build up of algae and placing the drinkers in the shade also helps.

DUBBING

The practice of dubbing has its roots in the cockfighting era. This involved the removing or certainly trimming down of the cockerel's comb, wattles and earlobes. Nowadays dubbing is still practised on Game breeds that are to be used for showing and it can be necessary to dub cockerels with large single combs who might be at risk from frostbite. There might also be a case for dubbing breeding cockerels where several are run together as it prevents extra grip if they start fighting. Dubbing can be done when males are day old chicks – the comb is cut with scissors and the chick shows no sign of stress. When older birds are dubbed and a razor blade or curved dubbing scissors are used, bleeding can be profuse and the procedure is much more stressful.

DUNG-HILL COCKS

This used to be a cocker or cock-fighter's term for the run-of-the-mill farmyard cockerels that were looked down upon as inferior to fighting cocks.

DUST BATHS

If chickens are confined, it is important that a dust bath is provided for them. A large box should be half-filled with dry earth, sand or ashes. If hens and cockerels are free ranging they will make dust baths for themselves in any areas of bare earth and craters will develop – dominant hens will often oust others from good dust bath spots. They like to squat down and shake themselves with movements of the body and wings so that their feathers get covered in dust. The dust trickles through their feathers and onto their skin. In this way they clean themselves and the dust helps remove many

of the parasites, such as lice, which infest the skin. Once finished, chickens will give their feathers a good shake and probably go back to searching for food.

DUTCH BANTAM

The Dutch Bantam originated in Holland but wasn't introduced to Britain until the 1960s. Available in a multitude of colours, these bantams are popular both as pets and exhibition birds. The Dutch Bantam is an alert, active bird with an upright jaunty appearance. Wings are carried low and although earlobes are white, the hens lay tinted eggs.

DUTCH BREEDS Named after places

The Welsummer is named after Welsum, the Barnevelder is named after the town of Barneveld and the Friesian after the region of Friesland. Breda, a rare breed in Britain, (also known as Kraaikoppen = crow-headed) is named after the town in Holland and the North Holland Blue, also rare in Britain, is named after the area. The Brabanter is another rare Dutch breed so called after Brabant which straddles Belgium and Holland.

See Barnevelder, Friesian, North Holland Blue, Welsummer

DUTCH POULTRY MUSEUM

This poultry museum is world famous and is based at Barneveld, which is also home to the Barnevelder breed. Visitors can see historic incubators, egg-sorting machines, hatching chicks and many Dutch breeds free ranging outside.

See Barnevelder

E

EGG

The egg is the age-old symbol of creation. Many ancient societies believed that the world was egg-shaped and was hatched from an egg made by God. The custom of presenting eggs is believed to have originated in Persia and was adopted by the Christians at Easter as a symbol of the resurrection of Christ, the eggs being coloured red in token of the blood of the redemption. The decoration of eggs for Easter is a traditional art in parts of Russia and eastern European countries such as Romania. Eggs used to be dyed various colours using onion skins, logwood, furze flowers and other wild flowers and herbs.

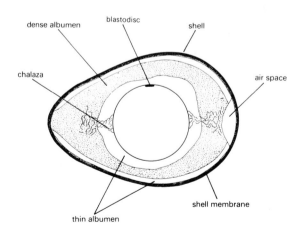

75

Eggs are the supreme gift from hens to human beings – the perfect food impeccably packaged, full of protein. The egg is one of the most versatile ingredients used in many dishes, both savoury and sweet. The white or albumen is nearly 88% water, 10% protein, .05% fat and .82% ash. The yolk is 49% water, 16.7% protein, 32% fat and 1.9% ash.

There is a 0.1% chance of an egg being double-yolked – ovulation occurs too quickly with one yolk getting lost and being joined by another one the next day; this is more common in young hens when starting to lay.

Eggs should be stored in their boxes to avoid absorption of different flavours through the shells and with large end up to keep the air cell in place and the yolk centred. Eggs can be stored in the fridge as they need a constant temperature but not in the egg trays in the door as, with the opening and shutting of the fridge, a constant temperature cannot be maintained. Eggs will be fine stored in a cool room. In any case they need to be brought up to room temperature before being cooked. Hard-boiled eggs will peel more easily if they are at least a week old. A cloudy white is a sign of freshness because of the high carbon dioxide content when the egg is laid. The carbon dioxide leaks out through the porous shell as the egg ages and this causes the protein in the egg to be reduced. Factory processes prevent this by dipping the eggs in a special oil which seals the pores of the shell thus preventing loss of moisture. In the Middle East eggs are cooked in a special way; whole eggs are simmered overnight in oil and onions. These are called Hamine Eggs (see separate entry).

See also Egg Laying, Egg Preserving, Egg-shells, Pace Eggs, Faberge Eggs, Proverbs, Brown Eggs versus White Eggs

 EGG AND I, THE

The Egg and I is a bestselling American book by Betty Macdonald which was published in 1945 and tells of her life married to Bob, on a chicken ranch in the Olympic Mountains in Washington State during the 1920s. The book was made into a film in 1946. Betty never found the life easy. The following passage gives a flavour of the book:

'Then I gathered the eggs. Gathering eggs would be like one continual Easter morning if the hens would just be obliging and get off the nests. Co-operation, however, is not a chickenly characteristic and so at egg-gathering time every nest was overflowing with hen, feet planted, and a shoot-if-you-must-this-old-grey-head look in her eye. I made all manner of futile attempts to dislodge her – sharp sticks, flapping apron, loud scary noises, lure of mash and grain – but she would merely set her mouth, clutch her eggs under her and dare me. In a way, I can't blame the hen – after all, soft-shelled or not, they're her kids.

The rooster, now, is something else again. He doesn't give a damn if you take every egg in the place and play handball. He doesn't care if the chicken house is knee-deep in weasels and blood. He just flicks a speck from his lapel and continues to stroll around, stepping daintily over the lifeless but still warm body of a former mistress, his lustful eye appraising the leg and breast of another quest.

Bob used to say that it was my approach to egg gathering which was wrong. I reached timidly under the hens and of course they pecked my wrists and as I jerked my hands away I broke the eggs or cracked them on the edges of the nests. Bob reached masterfully

77

under the hens and they gave without a murmur. I tried to assume this I-am-the-master attitude but I never for a moment fooled a hen and after three or four pecks I would be a bundle of chittering hysteria with the hens in complete command.'

The books ends with some memorable lines: 'I imagine that with lights and running water in the chicken houses we wouldn't have to get up until about seven or half-past'. 'Oh, that won't make any difference,' Bob said. 'Chickens have to be fed anyway and the earlier you feed 'em the sooner they start to lay.' Which just goes to show that a man in the chicken business is not his own boss at all. The hen is the boss.'

EGG BOUND

If a hen seems to be constantly going to the nest box but laying no eggs and shows signs of distress, it may be assumed that she is egg bound. The egg may be too large and will have got stuck, even though it is ready to be laid. A little oil can be inserted gently via a syringe into the vent as this may loosen the egg and allow it to be released. Another idea is to hold the bottom half of the hen carefully over steaming water for several minutes. This treatment generally relaxes and softens that part of the body, and the egg may then come out. If the egg breaks inside the hen it will probably kill her but she will also die if she cannot pass the egg.

EGGHEAD

Egghead was originally a word used in England for a bald man. In America in the fifties it was a word used to describe liberal intellectuals who supported the Democratic Presidential candidate, Adlai Stevenson – the skull of such an intellectual was thin and his brain was as soft as the inside of an egg!

EGG LAYING

The yolk of the egg is formed in the ovary and is then released to travel down the oviduct. In the longest part of the oviduct much of the albumen is added and also the cord-like chalazae which keep the yolk in place. The egg is driven down by peristaltic squeezing movements to the isthmus where it receives the shell membrane. It then moves to the uterus (shell gland) where it stays for about 20 hours while the shell-forming glands get to work. More albumen is added here and calcium is released as the main constituent of the shell. The shape and colour of the shell are also determined in the uterus. Finally the bloom or cuticle is added, the egg passes through the cloaca and is laid. In all, the egg has taken about 25 hours to form from ovulation to laying.

See also Bloom, Egg Bound, Laying Hens, Point of Lay

EGG PERITONITIS (INTERNAL LAYING)

Egg yolks drop into the body cavity, instead of entering the oviduct. This could happen if the bird is stressed at ovulation. In some cases the yolk will be scavenged by the body defences and the hen might survive. But sometimes several may descend together or infection sets in and the resulting peritonitis can quickly become fatal. The bird will have a swollen abdomen and be lethargic and depressed. She may waddle like a duck. Unfortunately there is not a lot that can be done.

EGG PRESERVING

There are three main ways eggs can be preserved.

a) Firstly they can be frozen. Raw eggs must be frozen out of their shells, either the yolks and whites separately or together. It is important that the eggs are very fresh as stale yolks are liable to

break. A little salt or sugar can be added to the separated yolks and then frozen in a suitable container. Separated whites can be frozen as they are, but cooked whites do not freeze well. Cooked yolks are okay frozen if incorporated into another dish. Whole raw eggs frozen in small containers can be fried or poached straight from the freezer.

b) Eggs can be stored for up to a year by putting them in waterglass solution (soluble sodium silicate). This seals the pores in the shell preventing the loss of moisture from the inside and keeps out bacteria. In other words, by storing eggs in waterglass, shells are made impervious. Fresh, unwashed, uncracked eggs should be used. Sodium silicate can be bought as a concentrated solution in a tin. It may be difficult to find as the demand is not great nowadays but old fashioned chemists or ironmongers may stock it – a 300ml tin of sodium silicate will be enough to preserve 80 eggs. Mix the sodium silicate powder with an equal part in weight of water and then this solution is diluted by one part to 20 parts of water. Earthenware jars or enamel buckets are the best containers to use. Fill with the solution and place the eggs carefully in the container, broad end uppermost with about 5cm of solution above the eggs. The container should be covered and since water will evaporate the solution will need to be topped up occasionally. To use eggs, wash them thoroughly under running cold water and prick them with a pin if they are to be boiled.

c) The third method is to pickle surplus eggs. First they need to be hard-boiled. For about 14 hard-boiled eggs use 900ml of white wine vinegar. Simmer the vinegar with a small piece of root ginger and a tablespoon of white peppercorns for about 15 minutes. Allow to cool and strain. Peel the eggs and arrange in a large glass jar.

Add one red chilli pepper and then pour on the spiced vinegar. Seal and leave for a couple of weeks before using.

EGG-SHELLS

The egg-shell is made up of calcium carbonate and protein and is porous (perforated all over with tiny holes) designed so that the developing chick can breathe. It is a remarkably complex structure consisting of several layers. Egg-shells can vary in colour from deep brown through to white with many shades of beige in between with or without a speckled effect. There are also the turquoise/green eggs laid by the Chilean breed, Araucana or Cream Legbar (the autosexing breed developed from the Araucana). There are some exceptions, but usually hens with white earlobes lay white eggs and hens with red earlobes lay brown eggs. The thickness of the shell is determined by the amount of time it spends in the shell gland (uterus) – if the egg-shell spends a short time in the uterus it will be thinner. The time of day also determines thickness – the earlier in the day that the egg-shell is formed the thicker it will be. The age of the hen can affect the quality of the shell – as she grows older the thinner the shell can become. The shell acquires its colour or pigment in the final stages of its development in the oviduct and only in the outer layer of the shell. The colour of the eggs laid by one hen also varies – as she continues to lay, eggs which started off dark brown may fade to a lighter brown.

EGG TOOTH

The egg tooth is the hard horny tip on the end of a newly hatched chick's beak. It is used by the chick to break its way out of the shell, known as pipping, and drops off soon after hatching.

EPONYMOUS BREEDS

Certain breeds are named after people: the Sebright Bantam is named after Sir John Sebright who developed it in the early 1800s; the Orloff, a Russian breed is named after Count Techesmensky; the Vorwerk, a German breed is named after Oskar Vorwerk who developed it in 1900. The Sultan was named because it originated in the Sultan of Constantinople's palace garden in Turkey and the Croad Langshan was named after Major Croad who imported Langshans to Britain.

See separate entries under individual breeds

 ESCAPE FROM COLD DITCH

This is a book by Alan Davidson upon which *Chicken Run*, the animated film was possibly based. The story tells of a hen, Fleur, who leads the escape of her fellow chickens from a battery farm. It is a retelling of the escape of British POWs from Colditz (the Nazi prison camp). Alan Davidson sued Aardman Animation and Dreamworks for copyright damages as the movie's plot was based on the book. The film also featured the same hens (although with different names) and the same rooster parachuting in to help out. The case did not come to trial. After three years of negotiations Mr Davidson filed a copyright infringement suit.

 ESCAPED COCK, THE by DH Lawrence

This is a short story also known as *The Man who Died*. Written in the late 1920s in the last years of his life, *The Escaped Cock* is a recasting of the resurrection of Christ. It begins:

There was a peasant near Jerusalem who acquired a young gamecock which looked a shabby little thing, but which put on brave feathers as spring advanced and was resplendent with arched and orange neck ... This peasant was poor ... He worked hard among the vines and olives and wheat of his master ... But he was proud of his young rooster. In the shut-in yard were three shabby hens which laid small eggs, shed the few feathers they had, and made a disproportionate amount of dirt ... The young cock grew to a certain splendour. By some freak of destiny, he was a dandy rooster, in that dirty little yard with three patchy hens. He learned to crane his neck and give shrill answers to the crowing of other cocks, beyond the walls, in a world he knew nothing of. But there was a special fiery colour to his crow, and the distant calling of the other cocks roused him to unexpected outbursts ...

'He will surely fly away one of these days,' said the peasant's wife. So they lured him with grain, caught him, though he fought with all his wings and feet, and they tied a cord round his shank, fastening it against the spur; and they tied the other end of the cord to the post that held up the donkey's straw pent-roof.

The young cock, freed, marched with a prancing stride of indignation away from the humans, came to the end of his string, gave a tug and a hitch of his tied leg, fell over for a moment, scuffled frantically on the unclean earthen floor, to the horror of the shabby hens, then with a sickening lurch, regained his feet, and stood to think. The peasant and the peasant's wife laughed heartily, and the young cock heard them. And he knew, with a gloomy, foreboding kind of knowledge, that he was tied by the leg ... He walked within the limits of his tether sombrely. Still he gobbled up the best bits of food. Still, sometimes, he saved an extra-best bit for his favourite

hen of the moment. Still he pranced with quivering, rocking fierceness upon such of his harem as came nonchalantly within range, and gave off the invisible lure. ... Underneath, however, the life in him was grimly unbroken. It was the cord that should break. So one morning, just before the light of dawn, rousing from his slumbers with a sudden wave of strength, he leaped forward on his wings, and the string snapped. He gave a wild strange squawk, rose in one lift to the top of the wall, and there he crowed a loud and splitting crow. So loud, it woke the peasant ...

'Advancing in a kind of half-consciousness under the dry stone wall of the olive orchard, the man was roused by the shrill, wild crowing of a cock just near him, a sound which made him shiver as if electricity had touched him. He saw a black and orange cock on a bough above the road, then running through the olives on the upper level, a peasant ... 'Oh stop him master, my escaped cock'! The man addressed, with a sudden flicker of smile, opened his great white wings of a shroud in front of the leaping bird. The cock fell back with a squawk and a flutter, the peasant jumped forward, there was a terrific beating of wings and whirring of feathers then the peasant had the escaped cock safely under his arm ...

[The man who had died accepted the peasant's hospitality and when it was time to leave] ... he gave the peasant a piece of money and said: 'Give me the cock that escaped and is now tied by the leg ... so the peasant gave the cock to the man ... and he came to an inn ... he saw the rooster of the inn walking forth to battle with his hens, a goodly number, behind him. Then the cock of the man who had died sprang forth and a battle began between the birds. The man of the inn ran to save his rooster but the man who had died said, 'If my bird wins I will give him thee. And if he

loses thou shall eat him.' So the birds fought savagely and the cock of the man who had died killed the common cock of the yard. ...'

See also, Lawrence, *Cocksure Women and Hensure Men*

EX-BATTERIES

Ex-battery hens can be rescued from the Battery Hen Welfare Trust (www.bhwt.org.uk) – they have co-ordinators all over Britain.

Other non-profit organisations are: Hen Rehomers (www.henrehomers.net) – they also have widespread co-ordinators, which means they have pick-up points across the country; Little Hen Rescue (www.littlehenrescue.co.uk) which is based in Norfolk and Free at Last (www.free-at-last.org.uk) based in Bedfordshire. Ex-battery hens can be tricky for beginners to look after since they need special treatment to start with. They may have lost a substantial amount of feathers, be unfit and unable to fly up on to a perch or into a nest box initially. They will invariably have been debeaked and so will find it more difficult to pick up food. The tip of the beak will probably not grow back at this stage. Hens will have large combs, often flopping over to one side which will be very pale and anaemic looking, beside a free range laying hen whose comb will be bright red. The combs become enlarged due to the heat in the battery units – they act as heat dissipaters. Hens will need a good sized hen house and run and should be confined for about 10 days so that they can build up strength and adapt to new surroundings. After that they should be given the chance to scratch, forage for food and have dust baths. If it rains they should be encouraged to take shelter. If ex-batteries are joining an established flock it is best to rescue hens that are not too badly defeathered as they will amalgamate with the other hens more easily. Hens with few feathers

will need several months to recover their feathers. Ex-battery hens should be fed growers pellets to start with as these have lots of protein. They will have only been fed layers mash while caged but will quickly adapt to a new diet. Later on they can be given layers pellets or mixed poultry corn and will enjoy kitchen scraps. If in good health ex-batteries should continue to lay every other day for at least another year.

See also Battery Hen Welfare Trust and Hen Rehomers

EXHIBITING POULTRY

Poultry shows are held across the country all year round with the three largest shows being the Poultry Club of Great Britain's National Championship Show at Stoneleigh in November, the National Federation of Poultry Club's Championship Show in Stafford in December and the Scottish National Poultry Show in Perth in January. Poultry are judged by breed and classification. Birds should be calm and used to sitting in cages – a flighty bird would not be suitable for showing. Birds, especially white-feathered ones, should be washed before a show with mild detergent, patted dry with a towel and finished with a hair drier. Vaseline can be used on feet once cleaned and on the comb.

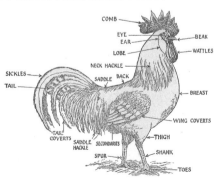

F

FABERGÉ EGGS

Peter Carl Fabergé was a businessman and jeweller living from
1846 to 1920. He created the House of Fabergé in St Petersburg
in 1870 and was commissioned by Tsar Nicholas II to produce
Imperial Eggs as presents for his wife Alexandra and his mother
Maria. The annual egg surprise lasted from 1895 to 1917 and 52
eggs were presented. Some bore the image of hens and cockerels.
The first egg was the Hen Egg made for Maria – it opened to
reveal a gold yolk holding a gold hen.

In 1903 the famous Chanticleer Egg was produced – Chanticleer
was made of gold with yellow, blue and green enamel and adorned
with diamonds – on the hour he would spring from the top of the
egg, nod his head, flap his wings and move his beak. The greatest
private collection of nine Fabergé Eggs was bought from the Forbes
Collection in America by a Russian billionaire, Victor Vekselberg
for at least $90 million so that they could be returned to Russia. It
is known that 10 eggs are in the Kremlin, three are owned by the
Queen, five are at the Virginia Museum of Fine Arts in America but
eight have an unknown whereabouts.

FANCY BREEDS

These are the pure breeds used principally for showing such as the
Frizzle, Sebrights, Yokohama and Hamburghs.

FAVEROLLES

The Faverolles originated from the village of Faverolles in northern France and was created from a mix of several different breeds, including the Dorking, Houdan and Cochin. Imported into the UK in 1886, producers of table chickens crossed the Faverolles with the Sussex, Orpington and Indian Game. The first true description of the breed came in 1893 and the salmon-coloured variation appeared later in 1895. They used to be bred specifically for meat production but they also produce a good number of eggs (tinted in colour) so are true dual-purpose birds. Colours vary from black, buff, cuckoo and ermine to salmon, which is probably the most popular. The birds have a broad, square body with small wings, a single upright comb, short neck, a striking beard and muffling. The pinkish legs are sparsely feathered with the feathering concentrated on the outer toe. They have five toes, the fifth one points upwards. Quiet, friendly birds that are an ideal breed for children, the hens make very good broodies and mothers. Bantam versions are also available.

FAYOUMI

This is a rare Egyptian breed from the district of Fayoum (meaning water) south of Cairo. Fayoumis have been raised along the Nile since early times existing as free range scavengers. They were introduced into Britain in 1984 by the Domestic Fowl Trust. Fayoumis are hardy, attractive and can be silver or gold-pencilled. The hens lay white eggs. No other breed matures as quickly as the Fayoumi

– pullets may start to lay small eggs at four months and the cockerels may start to crow at rather an unbelievable six weeks old! Both hens and cockerels are very flighty so not ideal for small gardens. The cockerels are striking-looking birds when their sickle feathers are fully formed and they have jet black, piercing eyes. Fayoumis are not a beginner's bird. The large fowl Fayoumis are relatively small and bantam versions are available.

FEATHERED LEGS
Several breeds sport feathered legs – the little Pekins have heavily feathered legs which prevent them from scratching up too much soil. Other breeds include the Cochin (large version of the Pekin), French Marans, Brahma, Faverolles, Sultan, Langshan, Barbu d'Uccle and Booted Bantam (Sablepoot).

FEATHER PECKING
Feather pecking between hens can be a real problem and is especially common if hens are confined in a small space. There are sprays available to use on affected bare areas that will put the culprits off pecking out more feathers. The feathers won't regrow while a hen is in constant egg production and it may not be until moulting in the autumn that a hen will replace lost feathers.

FEATHERS AND FEATHER MARKINGS
Feathers cover almost all breeds of poultry with the exception of Silkies who are covered by down and of course there are no feathers on the neck of the Transylvanian Naked Neck. Feathers are shed during the moulting process in the autumn and new feathers sometimes of a slightly different shade will regrow reasonably quickly. The undeveloped feathers which form short stubs are

known as pin feathers. Feathers on different breeds can have beautiful colours and patterns. Feathers can be: **barred** – alternate stripes of light and dark across the feather; **cuckoo** – irregular banding where two colours are difficult to distinguish and run into each other as on the Cuckoo Marans; **laced** – a stripe around the edge of a feather; **double-laced** – two layers of lacing, one on the outer edge of the feather and then an inner one – these could be black or brown; **pencilled** – small stripes going across on a feather or concentric following the outline of the feather; **spangled** – a spot of different colour at the end of each feather; **splashed** – a contrasting colour unevenly displayed on the feather; **mottled** – marked with tips or spots of different colour. Feathers on each hen have differing textures and size.

Clockwise from top left: self, tipping, spangling, barring, striping, double-lacing, single-lacing, peppering, pencilling.

Down-type feathers, also known as fluff, tend to cover the backside of many hens. Primaries or flight feathers are elongated and stiff to provide lift when a chicken uses its wings to flap or fly. The secondaries are the inner quills on the wings. The axial feather separates the secondary and primary feathers on each wing. The cockerel has hackles which are feathers on his neck, saddle and on his back just in front of the tail and sickles which are his long curved tail feathers. On the hen this area of feathers in front of the tail is called the cushion because of its softness. A squirrel tail is the name for feathers which are carried too high and a wry tail is carried to one side; both are defects in a cockerel which is intended for breeding or showing. Different breeds are known as hard-feathered or soft-feathered.

See Colours, Moulting, Wing clipping

FEEDING

A normal sized hen needs about 120g of food a day in the form of grain. This can be supplied as mixed poultry grain, layers pellets or layers mash. Mixed grain consists of wheat, barley, oats and maize (it is the maize, which along with grass, produces the yellow pigment found in egg yolks). For pellets and mash these grains are ground down. Pellets are small and cylindrical – they are clean and easy for hens to eat but if confined the hens can get bored. Mash on the other hand keeps the birds busy for hours and can be fed dry or wet. For chicks the grains are ground down to form crumbs. Chick crumbs also contain a coccidiostat as an aid in the prevention of a disease known as coccidiosis. From about eight weeks chicks (known as Growers until they become Point of Lay at between 18 and 22 weeks) can be given growers pellets and these fill the gap between chick crumbs and mixed grain or layers pellets. Free range

hens will forage during the day, eating insects and worms, grass and other green-stuff. They will also enjoy some kitchen scraps such as left-over cooked pasta and rice, bread, bits of pastry, cooked potatoes and other vegetables and lettuce leaves. Most hens also enjoy bananas and fruit with pips, tomatoes, sunflower seeds, and bits of hard cheese. Kitchen scraps to be avoided are anything salty, citrus peel, banana skins, uncooked potato peelings, chocolate and fish bones. Hens producing eggs on a regular basis also need calcium in their diet. If they live on chalky soil they may be able to pick up enough from the soil. But if the shells on their eggs are particularly thin then their diet should be supplemented with extra calcium. Crushed oyster or cockle shells, sometimes with grit added, can be bought from feed merchants or egg-shells can be baked and crushed and fed directly (baking prevents hens getting a taste for fresh egg-shells). Grit is needed because it helps hens digest food when it reaches the gizzard, and free range hens can pick this up from the soil. Covered feed hoppers can be used to give hens access to their food which should be available to them all day. Feed should be kept in dustbins or containers with lids to avoid the possibility of rats, mice or badgers getting to it.

FIVE-TOED BREEDS

There are six breeds which have five toes instead of the more conventional four. These are most famously the Dorking but also the Houdan, Faverolles, Silkie, Sultan and the Lincolnshire Buff.

 ## FOGHORN LEGHORN

Foghorn Leghorn was a large rooster cartoon character appearing in Warner Bros cartoons such as *Crowing Pains, Of Rice and Hen, and Pullet Surprise* as far back as 1946.

FOLKLORE

There is quite a lot of folklore surrounding setting eggs (i.e. putting them to incubate under a hen), as in the past this had overtones of fertility rituals. Until the late 19th Century it was thought unwise to carry fertile eggs over streams or to set them on a Sunday or in May (the month of witchcraft). Spring flowers could badly affect hatching and if less than 13 primroses were brought into the house then that was the number of eggs that would hatch – each primrose represented one chick. It is still believed that only an odd number of eggs should be set, at the moon's increase for success and at sunset in order to hatch pullets. Once chicks were hatched, a lighted candle would be passed over them to save them from predator attacks. The last egg laid by an old hen was kept as a fertility charm while a white pullet's first egg was good news and the luckiest present for a country sweetheart. The small cock or witch egg (see cock's egg) was an ill omen and the hen who laid it, was killed. It was thought to be bad luck to bring eggs into the house after dark. After eating a boiled egg the shell should be crushed and a spoon pushed through the bottom to avoid bad luck.

 FOLKTALES

There are various folktales from around the world featuring mainly cockerels. *The Cock and the Centipede* is a Chinese tale telling of a cock endowed with antlers, who, after much persuasion, lends them to a dragon to wear at the Emperor's banquet – the centipede guarantees their safety – however after the banquet the dragon refuses to give them back and the cock is so angry he pecks the centipede in half; ever since the cock and centipede have been arch enemies. *The Cock and the Handmill* is similar to *Jack and*

the Beanstalk; a poor man climbs an oak tree and finds a handmill and a cock with a beautiful golden comb. The handmill produces pancakes and pies which are shared with the cock. Then a rich man steals it. The cock sets out to get it back and eventually arrives in the rich man's dining room and crows: 'Give us back our handmill' – all his guests are so petrified they run off and the cock returns the handmill to the old man and woman. An African folktale tells the story of *The Crocodile and the Hen* – the crocodile announces to his friend the lizard: 'I caught a hen by the river, but when I wanted to eat her she shrieked that I should let her go and called me her dear brother. Am I the brother of a hen?' The lizard laughed. 'The hen was telling the truth. Don't you know that hens are hatched out of eggs, just as crocodiles are?' The crocodile nodded. 'You are quite right. I had never thought about it before. If you look at it that way the hen really is my sister, or at least my niece.' And ever afterwards the crocodile left hens in peace. A little known American folktale, *The Talking Eggs*, tells the story of two sisters, good Blanche and bad Millison – Blanche does the right thing with the talking eggs, not taking the gold ones, and makes her fortune. Millison is greedy and takes the gold eggs – when she breaks them, out come snakes, toads, frogs and swarms of mosquitoes.

How the Cock Became a Domestic Bird (Australian)

This tells the story of Cockadoodle, chieftain of the birds who lives with all the birds in a village on the slopes of a high mountain. But one day their fire goes out and the brave cock promises to bring them new fire. He flies off and finds a beautiful girl with black hair and eyes like stars sitting in a house by a fire. She thinks Cockadoodle is very handsome and says she would like him as a

94

husband. But the cock doesn't want to marry, takes a branch from the fire and flies off, saying only, 'you will find me far away in a village in the mountains living with all the birds.' The girl and her parents set off to find him. They find the village and lure Cockadoodle to their boat full of coconuts, throw a net over him and row off back to their cottage by the sea. Since that time the cock has lived among people. The other birds dispersed and found new homes.

The Old Woman, the Hen and the Dog (Italian)

An old woman lives happily with her dog and hen – she cooks, the hen lays eggs and the dog guards the cottage. Then one day the hen stops laying eggs and they have nothing to eat. A monk drops by and offers to help by taking the hen away and teaching her to lay eggs again. But the dog knows better – the monk is a fox dressed in a monk's habit and sees him off. Next a rag and bone man calls and offers to do the same as the monk but the dog knows this is a marten dressed up and sees him off. Lastly a pedlar appears with a basket of nuts – this time it's a wolf – the dog sees him off but the wolf drops his basket. The hen eats the nuts for three days and starts laying eggs again!

The Little Half-chick (Spanish)

This tells of a Spanish hen whose last chick to hatch came out as half a chicken with one leg, one wing and one eye. He was bold and headstrong and decided to go to Madrid to visit the King. On the way he met the stream who asked for help but he refused; he met a fire, he met a wind, both of whom he refused to help. When he reached the King's palace he was spotted and was thrown into a pot to be cooked for the king's dinner. The water came over the

95

little half chick and he asked for the water not to drown him; the fire blazed and he asked the fire not to burn him but the fire wouldn't help. When he was burnt to a cinder he was thrown out of the window and the wind blew him up, round and round he twirled, crying for help from the wind. But the wind said: 'when I was in trouble you wouldn't help me' and blew him right up to the top of the highest church and left him stuck to the top of the steeple. The little half-chick is still there today, one wing hangs drooping at his side and he looks out over the city with one eye as he turns slowly round when the wind blows.

The Brave Half-a-cockerel and the King (Spanish)

Two old women divide their cockerel in half. One makes soup and the other lets her half run about in the yard. It finds a purse of gold sovereigns on a dunghill. But the King drives past in his coach and his servants grab the purse. Half-a-cockerel sets off to retrieve it. He meets a fox, a swarm of wasps and a river which all grow tired and climb under the Half-a-cockerel's wing. He arrives at the castle but the servants, on the King's orders, put him in a coop full of chickens hoping he will be pecked to death. But the cock calls on the fox to come out and he kills the chickens. Again Half-a-cockerel asks the King for his purse. The King puts him on his throne and sits on him but the wasps come out and sting the King. Next the King puts the cock in the oven, hoping to have roast cockerel in the morning. But the river comes out and floods the oven, kitchen and castle. The King, fearful of drowning, climbs onto his roof and realising he has been out-witted, gives Half-a-cockerel back his purse. He rushes back to the old woman and to this day runs happily around, pecking, scratching and crowing.

The Cock and the Crested Hen (English)

There was once a Cock who had a whole farmyard of hens to look after; and among them was a tiny little Crested Hen. She thought she was altogether too grand to be in company with the other hens, for they looked so old and shabby; she wanted to go out and strut about all by herself, so that people could see how fine she was, and admire her pretty crest and beautiful plumage. So one day when all the hens were strutting about on the dust-heap and showing themselves off, the desire seized her, and she cried: 'Cluck, cluck, cluck, over the fence!' and wanted to get away. The Cock stretched his neck and shook his comb and feathers and cried: 'Go not there!' And all the old hens cackled: 'Go-go-go not there! But she still set off and was not a little proud when she got away, and could go about pluming and showing herself off quite alone. Just then a hawk began to fly round above her, and all of a sudden he swooped down upon her. The Cock, as he stood on top of the dust-heap, stretching his neck and peering first with one eye and then with the other, had long noticed him, and cried with all his might: 'Come, come, come and help!' till the people came running. The frightened hawk let go of the Hen, and had to be satisfied with her tuft and her finest feathers, which he had plucked from her. And she lost no time in running home; she stretched her neck, and tripped along, crying: 'See, see, see, how I look!' The Cock came up to her in his dignified way, drooped one of his wings, and said: 'Didn't I tell you?' From that time the Hen did not consider herself too good to be with the old hens on the dust-heap.

The Black Hen (English)

A great many years ago, there was a large fairy ring of particularly lush green grass in one of the meadows of a certain remote parish on the western fringe of Dartmoor, and within this magic circle a jet black hen and chicks were occasionally seen at nightfall. The vicar of the parish was an extremely keen student of sorcery and possessed a large collection of books and manuscripts dealing with the perilous subject of black magic. One day while the parson was conducting a service in the village church, one of his servants happened to visit his study and finding a large volume lying open on the table, began to read it aloud. He had read no more than half a page when the sky became dark and the house was shaken violently by a great wind. The servant, deeply absorbed in the book, read on; and as the storm increased in fury, the door flew open and a black hen and chicks entered the room. The creatures were of normal size when they first appeared but they gradually grew larger and larger until the hen became as big as a prize bullock. At this point the vicar, who was in the midst of his sermon in the pulpit of the church, suddenly closed his discourse, and abruptly dismissed the astonished congregation, saying that he was needed at home urgently and hoped he would arrive there in time. When he entered the study the hen had grown so large that she was touching the ceiling. He quickly threw down a bag of rice which stood ready in a corner of the room and while the hen and chicks were busily engaged in picking up the grains he had time to reverse the spell.

The Hen and the Hawk (Philippine)

A hawk flying about in the sky one day decided that he wanted to marry a hen whom he often saw on earth. He flew down and asked her to become his wife. She at once gave her consent if he would wait until she could grow wings like his, so that she might also fly high. The hawk agreed to this and flew away, after giving her an engagement ring and telling her to take good care of it. The hen was very proud of the ring and placed it around her neck. The next day, however, she met the resident cock who looked at her in astonishment and said: 'Where did you get that ring? Do you not know that you promised to be my wife? You must not wear the ring of anybody else. Throw it away.' And the hen threw away the beautiful ring. Not long after this the hawk came down bringing beautiful feathers to dress the hen. When she saw him coming she was frightened and ran to hide, but the hawk called to her to come and see the beautiful dress. The hen came out, and the hawk at once saw that the ring was gone. 'Where is it?' he asked. The hen was ashamed to tell the truth so she answered: 'Oh, sir, yesterday when I was walking in the garden, I met a large snake and he frightened me so that I ran as fast as I could to the house. Then I missed the ring and I searched everywhere but could not find it.' The hawk looked sharply at the hen, and he knew that she was deceiving him and said: 'How could you behave so badly? When you have found the ring I will come down again and make you my wife. But as punishment for breaking your promise, you must always scratch the ground to look for the ring. And every chick of yours that I find, I shall snatch away.' Then he flew away, and ever since all the hens throughout the world have been scratching to find the hawk's ring.

FOSTER MOTHERS

Certain breeds of hens, especially Silkies, make great foster mothers. They will sit on duck or even guinea fowl eggs, hatch and care for the chicks. Here are two fictional extracts:

 ### A Duck to Water by G B Stern (1949)

'Eleven black ducklings, however lovable, were bound to be a shock to the mothering hen, who naturally had not expected anything quite so absurd to emerge from the dim warm eggs that had somehow come to mean so much to her during the long days and weeks they had been left undisturbed in the straw of the hen house. When the Feeding Legs came across the bridge from the garden to the meadow to feed the ducks, hens and geese, rattling the corn in the saucepan, the brown mother hen still would not leave her eggs, no, not for all the corn in the world … so they left her alone and her prettier sister Rhoda in the next door box … and the Feeding Legs exclaimed: 'Why Rhoda's beaten you to it, after all! … five lively little packets of yellow fluff; five greedy squeaking little chicks opening and shutting their pointed beaks in a desperate hurry to be fed and to grow and be fed again and again … Meanwhile Rhoda paraded her chicks in front of her quiet brown sister-hen and called her a slowcoach and a lazybones. But that did not matter … Beneath her were strange little sounds and stirrings; all was not as quiet as it had been before; then a shell cracked; and another shell – tough shells, tougher than seemed perfectly right … and the brown hen was never able to remember the exact moment when a vague premonition seized her. She was a reserved little soul and confided in no one. And things were happening too fast now to reverse time … but what was this brood, greyish black, with long narrow heads

and webbed mackintosh feet and flat hard protruding beaks? Beaks squawking with all their might, grotesque and yet appealing – Could they be chickens, one day to grow into hens like herself? Could they indeed be the result of that long unbroken vigilance, crouching deep in the straw to keep life warm? … I hope the Feeding Legs won't be disappointed … But the Feeding Legs was exultant … 'Eleven! My word!' and gave bread and milk to that absurd wobbling little brood of blacks with the huge heads and webbed feet … and the brown hen watched over her eleven little grotesques with all the care and tenderness she would have given a fairer, more accountable brood; scolding them when they strayed – and small as they were they always seemed to be straying … A fortnight later she had a further trial to bear: another, an elder sister parading her chicks, yellow, fluffy and correct … 'Do you know what they remind me of, a little in shape,' said her sister. 'No I don't, replied the brown hen in a great hurry. And then she added, 'I don't care what you all say; I never went near the Sheldrake!'

The Hen that Hatched Ducks

A little known short story (1867) by Harriet Beecher Stowe, the American authoress of *Uncle Tom's Cabin* begins:

'Once there was a nice young hen that we will call Mrs Feathertop. She was a hen of most excellent family, being a direct descendant of the Bolton Grays, and as pretty a young fowl as you could wish to see on a summer's day. She was, moreover, as fortunately situated in life as it was possible for a hen to be. She was bought by young Master Fred Little John, with four or five family connections of hers, and a lively young cock, who was held to be

as brisk a scratcher and as capable a head of a family as any half-dozen sensible hens could desire.

I can't say that at first Mrs Feathertop was a very sensible hen. She was very pretty and lively and a great favourite with Master Bolton Gray Cock, on account of her bright eyes, her finely shaded feathers, and certain saucy dashing ways that she had which seemed greatly to take his fancy. But old Mrs Scratchard, living in the neighbouring yard, assured all the neighbourhood that Gray Cock was a fool for thinking so much of that flighty young thing; that she had not the smallest notion how to get on in life, and thought of nothing in the world but her own pretty feathers. 'Wait till she comes to have chicks,' said Mrs Scratchard; 'then you will see. I have brought up ten broods myself – as likely and respectable chicks as ever were a blessing to society – and I think I ought to know a good hatcher and brooder when I see her; and I know THAT fine piece of trumpery, with her white feathers tipped with grey, never will come down to family life. She scratch for chicks! Bless me, she never did anything in all her days but run round and eat the worms which somebody else scratched up for her.'

The story continues with Master Freddy being given eight ducks' eggs to put under Mrs Feathertop. She hatches her ducklings ... 'at first it was thought they were deformed by other members of the farmyard with their strange bills which greatly alarmed Mrs Feathertop and Dr Peppercorn was called for; he recommended various remedies ... in the meantime the ducklings wore Mrs Feathertop out – the ducklings with 'saucepans on the end of their noses' and who 'took every opportunity to waddle their little ways down to the mud and water'... and ... 'with a dreadful sort of madness which makes them love to shovel mud with those shocking spoon-bills' ... *And then one day the ducks*

all go swimming. Dr Partlett is called to tell Mrs Feathertop about her ducklings 'At this moment a quack was heard, and at a distance the whole tribe were seen coming waddling home, their feathers gleaming in green and gold, and they themselves in high good spirits. 'Such a splendid day as we have had!' they all cried in a breath … And so Madam Feathertop came off glorious at last.'

FOWL HOUSE, THE

The Fowl House was built in 1861 by John Naylor of Leighton Hall as a birthday present for his daughter Georgina. Mr Naylor had this luxurious Fowl House built to house a collection of exotic and ornamental birds – hens, ducks, geese, turkeys and doves.

The fowl were accommodated in discreet apartments according to breed and had tiered roosts, pop-holes and a scratching yard with storm shelter for rainy days. Naylor's architect W H Gee of Liverpool spared no expense and paid great attention to detail installing beautiful windows and door furniture. The design may

have been inspired by Queen Victoria's Poultry Houses at Windsor. The everyday care of the birds was under the supervision of a Poultry Keeper who lived in a cottage adjacent to the yard. Both the Poultry Cottage and The Fowl House now belong to the Landmark Trust, a charity which restores neglected historic buildings and gives them a new future by offering them for holidays.

See Victoria, Queen

FOXES

Foxes are the most common and dangerous killers of hens and usually strike first thing in the morning or at dusk, although in urban areas foxes can be seen during the day. One often hears stories of foxes killing all the hens a family owns in one go. People wonder why a fox kills every hen in sight and only carries off one or two. He only does this because he runs out of time: left to his own devices he would come back and carry off each carcass to bury as food for the future. He is an opportunist and cleverer than we suppose. Foxes can leap over walls and fences under 2m in height and dig under runs. Electric fencing will keep foxes out. Otherwise ordinary fencing should be at least 2m high and wire should be dug 30cm into the ground. Hens should be locked into secure hen houses at night. Foxes hate human smells and sounds so preventative measures include hanging balls of human hair or a switched on radio near the run, or sprinkling human urine in the relevant area.

FREE RANGE AND ORGANIC EGGS

According the British Egg Information Service 38% of eggs are now produced by free range or organic laying hens. 'Free Range' means hens are kept in large sheds with access to the outside, however with at least 1,000 in a flock some hens never actually

venture outside. Organic eggs account for about 5% of this total. The Soil Association has strict rules for organic certification – flocks must be 2,000 or less.

FREEWAY CHICKENS
This was a colony of chickens who lived under the Hollywood Freeway of Los Angeles. Rumour has it that a poultry truck overturned in 1969 – hundreds of chickens were lost, some were killed but those that survived set up permanent residence under the Freeway. The mystery is that these hens were on their way to slaughter so no-one is quite certain how they multiplied with no cockerels present and were still there in the late seventies.

FRENCH BREEDS Named after places
Marans, Houdan, Faverolles, La Flèche, La Bresse and Crevècoeur are all named after French locations and apart from Marans all are in the north west corner of France. Marans is a small port near La Rochelle in western France. Houdan is a small town in Normandy just west of Paris. Faverolles is a village not far from Houdan. La Flèche is a small town in the Loire and Bourg-en-Bresse is a town in east France north of Lyon which is twinned with Aylesbury in Buckinghamshire. Crevècoeur is a village near Caen in Normandy.
See Bresse, Faverolles, Houdan, La Flèche, Marans

FRIESIAN FOWL
The Friesian is an attractive Dutch breed and although classed as large fowl is bantam-sized. Friesians are active and flighty, with hens laying white eggs and can be gold, silver or chamois pencilled.

FRIZZLE

Frizzles reportedly originated in southern Asia, in particular the Philippines and Java around 300 years ago but examples were actually documented in Europe in 1676. These only had frizzled wings and neck hackles, though. The breed is very popular for exhibition, usually in the bantam form. The large fowl was virtually extinct until a handful of enthusiasts recently started a breeding programme to revive it. They are now considered to be a rare breed. The birds are called Frizzles because their feathers, which are moderately long, curl backwards towards the bird's head. The individual feathers have a rather ragged appearance and the neck has abundant frizzled feathers. Frizzles are erect birds with short bodies, long wings, upright tails and single combs. The chicks appear to be normally feathered when they are hatched but the wing feathers soon start to grow and turn outwards. Good layers who don't go broody too easily, Frizzles are classed as a heavy breed with large fowl and bantams available. They can be black, blue, buff, white Columbian, duckwing, black-red, cuckoo or pyle. There are three types of plumage: frizzled, over frizzled and flat-coated.

G

GAINESVILLE

The city of Gainesville in Georgia, US was renowned for its poultry processing plants and is known as the Chicken Capital of the World.

GALLIC ROOSTER - LE COQ GAULOIS

The Gallic Rooster is a national symbol of France. Its association is due to the play on words in Latin between Gallia, which was what Caesar named France, and Gallus meaning cockerel. The rooster was used as an ornament on church bell towers in the Middle Ages as a symbol of vigilance due to his crowing at sunrise. The rooster emblem gained particular popularity during the French Revolution. Since 1848 he has featured on the Great Seal of France (the Official Seal of the French Republic) depicted on a ship's rudder next to the figure of Liberty. Today he is often used as a national mascot in sporting events and is the emblem of sponsored French sports teams.

See also Diomede

GAME FOWL

There are several breeds of Game Fowl. These were originally used for cockfighting; the two chief ones now kept in Britain for poultry purposes are Indian Game and Old English Game (see separate entries). The Asil is an old breed of Game Fowl (see separate entry).

GEORGE

George is a black Wyandotte cockerel who was at the centre of a council probe in 2009 for his incessant early-morning crowing. One recording showed George crowing 73 times in just 16 minutes one morning. But owner Lee Spensley hopes he has solved the problem by blocking out the light into George's hutch until he is released at 7.30am. Mr Spensley found it unbelievable that Staffordshire Borough Council spent a week recording George's crowing from his garden in the hamlet of Hatton, near Eccleshall. He then got a letter informing him that excessive noise had been detected at his property. The letter said: 'The monitored noise was indicative of a statutory nuisance. Therefore, it is requested that your co-operation is received in preventing the need for further action.' Mr Spensley says the council's response was 'over the top'. He said: 'They should have just come to me. It is something I would have very easily solved – there was no need for secretive monitoring. To send several letters and have someone come out and use recording equipment for one cockerel seems excessive. I live in a rural area and believe the recordings picked up other birds including geese.' Mr Spensley's partner added: 'George has never disturbed me. He's quiet compared to the noise from cars and motorbikes on the road. He's been on the street for years so I don't know why there's suddenly been a complaint now.' At least this case was resolved without the need for court proceedings.
See also Crowing, Corky, Victoire

GIPSEY

Gipsey was a famous fighting cock bred by George Wilson in Stuart times who had great successes in the cockpit in Bury St Edmunds. He fought so courageously in many battles that his master had his

picture painted on cloth with the words 'O noble Gipsey such a cock art thou, As Bury town did ne'er contain till now: wherefore to praise thy worth and spread thy fame, we make this show in honour of thy name.' The cock was put in a cage and paraded through the town with the cloth carried before him.

GIZZARD

Food that has been stored in the crop passes through the stomach and then arrives in the gizzard where it is ground into a paste – the gizzard making up for the lack of teeth.
See Crop

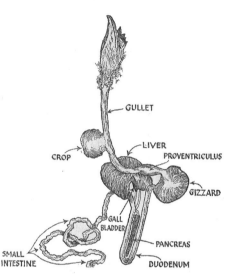

GOLDTOP BANTAMS

These are a cross between white Silkie males and light Sussex females. Goldtop is not technically a true name but this seems to be the popular name for the cross – in different regions Goldtops are also known as Clockers, Cluckers or Tufties. They are pretty (buff coloured with some black on the neck and with crests), very friendly and go broody easily so make excellent mothers. The cross produces sex-linked chicks which means the males and females have different markings so can be identified when hatched.

GRIT see Feeding

H

HACKLES

Hackles are the neck and saddle feathers on a cockerel. They are long, narrow pointed feathers.

HAMBURGH

Nobody knows where
Hamburghs originated
– Holland, the UK or
Germany have all been
suggested. Hamburghs are
rose-combed with white
earlobes, slate legs and long

bodies. They are light, soft-feathered birds available in very attractive colours – gold, silver or black. The gold and silver can be pencilled (with pencilling straight across in fine parallel lines of rich green-black) or spangled (black tip to the feather). The bantams are miniature versions of the large fowl but have not been bred in black. Hamburghs are lively, active birds and difficult to tame because they are quite flighty. They lay white eggs and are generally non-sitters.

HAMINE EGGS

These are eggs that have been simmered in water for at least six hours. Eggs cooked for a long time in this way will have yolks that

turn from hard and crumbly to unbelievably creamy and soft. This is traditionally an Egyptian method for serving eggs called Beid Hamine with origins in the ancient Jewish community. The long cooking time comes from the Jewish tradition of slow cooking food overnight to serve on Shabbat, when cooking is forbidden. These eggs are cooked in water with onion skins (this turns the egg whites brown) and a little oil. A tablespoon of ground coffee can also be added to give the eggs the desired brown colour. Eggs can be stored in this state for years.

HANDLING POULTRY

To hold a bird correctly the palm of one's hand should be slipped under the breast and with legs held between the fingers her head faces one's bent elbow. The other hand is free to place on the back to balance or examine the bird. Poultry should not be held upside down by one or both legs.

HARD-FEATHERED BREEDS

The game breeds such as Asil, Old English and Modern Game are classified as hard-feathered. The feathering is tight and closely knit.

HARUSPICY

A form of divination practised by the Romans which involved the reading of chicken entrails that had been sacrificed to foretell the future.

HATCHERY

A hatchery is a factory unit used for hatching out chicks. Hatcheries are used to hatch broilers (for meat) or layers. Hatcheries for layers

across Britain produce around 30 million female chicks that will become laying hens every year. At least the same number of unwanted male chicks are disposed of each year, either by gassing or IMD (Instantaneous Mechanical Destruction); dislocation of the neck is also permitted in an emergency. In the US it has been revealed that chicks are not always disposed of so humanely. One of the biggest hatcheries is the Hy-Line hatchery in Iowa. Chicks here are hatched and processed by being dumped on conveyor belts. The male chicks have been recorded as being ground up while still alive.

HATCHING EGGS

This is the term used for fertile eggs which will hatch chicks if put under a broody hen – they can be bought from breeders directly or on eBay.

HEAVY BREEDS

Heavy Breeds are historically those developed for table or utility production, many of them having a good reputation for egg laying. The majority of heavy breeds have an excellent temperament, which makes them suitable for a variety of purposes and ideal for beginners or children. Examples of heavy breeds are Barnevelder, Brahma, Orpington, Marans, Plymouth Rock, Rhode Island Red, Sussex and Wyandotte.

HEN REHOMERS

Hen Rehomers (www.henrehomers.net) are a non-profit organisation who depend entirely on donations for their good work. They purchase hens from farmers just before the slaughter date

and with co-ordinators across the country manage to re-home about 2,000 hens every two months. In 2009 they re-homed nearly 12,000 hens. Volunteers collect the hens, carefully loading them into crates and drive them to distribution points across the country. At present they charge a minimum of £1.50 per bird to those wanting to rescue hens.

 HEN TALES FOR CHILDREN

The best known stories regarding hens are probably *The Little Red Hen* and *Chicken Licken*. *The Little Red Hen* is about a hen who wants help to plant grains of wheat but the cat, rat and pig won't help; they also refuse to help cut the wheat, take it to the mill to be ground into flour and take the flour to the baker. When Little Red Hen returns with the bread they all want to help her eat it. Very sensibly she eats the lot herself.

Chicken Licken has a sad ending since Chicken Licken, Henny Penny, Cocky Locky, Ducky Lucky, Drakey Lakey, Goosey Loosey, and Turkey Lurkey are all on the way to tell the King that the Sky is falling down when they meet Foxy Loxy who leads them straight to his den where he and his family eat the lot of them.

Then there is the familiar English folktale, *The Sly Fox and the Little Red Hen* which tells the story of the fox who is always trying to catch Little Red Hen. One day he sneaks into her house – she flies onto a beam and he whirls round and round making the hen dizzy – she then falls into his bag. But later she outwits the fox when he falls asleep and she escapes, filling his bag with heavy stones. The stones are tipped into a pot of boiling water which spills over the fox and his mother, killing them. The variation on this

story is *The Cockerel, the Mouse and the Little Red Hen* in which Little Red Hen does all the chores; the fox arrives and puts all three of them in his sack; the hen effects their escape with her sewing kit, fills the bag with stones and the fox falls into a stream; after that cock and mouse do the chores!

It's Perfectly True by Hans Christian Andersen is an allegory about a hen who decides that the more feathers she plucks from her body the more beautiful she will become. When one of her feathers happens to fall out a malicious hen starts a rumour which becomes exaggerated – two hens are plucking their feathers and then three hens have died of unrequited love. The rumours go back to the original hen house saying that five hens have plucked out all their feathers and have pecked each other to death.

In the Brothers Grimm tale, *The House in the Wood,* a Brindled Cow, Hen and Cock live with an old man – it is only when the woodcutter's third daughter prepares a meal and includes food for the animals that the spell that was cast upon the King's son by a wicked witch is broken and the old man becomes the King's son again – the Cow, Hen and Cock are transformed back into his servants. The first and second daughters are punished for letting the animals suffer and do penance as servants to a collier until reformed. A more recent hen story has been written by Dick King Smith, entitled *The Fox Busters* (1978) and is a humorous tale about three hens Ransome, Sims and Jefferies of Foxearth Farm who devise cunning plans to outwit the wily fox in his never-ending quest to kill and eat chicken.

Modern tales for young children include *Queenie the Bantam* by Bob Graham (1999), *Hattie and the Fox* by Mem Fox (1987), *Henry and the Fox* which is about a cowardly cockerel but also

features Buffy the bantam and is by Chris Wormell (2007) and *Ethel the Hen* by Colin Thompson (1991). Jill Tomlinson also wrote a longer story called *The Hen who Wouldn't Give Up* (2004) about a determined, speckled hen called Hilda who hitches a lift to see her Aunt's chicks and eventually hatches her own brood.

The following story illustrates perfectly why a cockerel and his hens should be given a nice home and happy free range life in exchange for at least some of the hens' eggs:

The Cockerel and the Hens (from *The Black Aunt – Stories and Legends for Children* translated from German, 1848)
There was once a great farmyard in which there lived a splendid looking Cockerel with his wives, a whole flock of hens, black and white, grey and brown, both with and without crests. They all lived in great peace and harmony for everything went well with them and every day they got a large pile of barley-corns for their food.

Only one thing troubled them, that their eggs were always taken away and they could hardly ever bring up a brood of chicks. The hens often hid their nests, sometimes in the woodshed, sometimes in the barn, so that the eggs might not be found, and once they had actually saved up a mountain of eggs. But the girl who fed them found their egg mountain and carried it to the city and sold it. Indeed it was no more than natural that the eggs should be found, for as soon as a hen had laid one, she set up such a cackling that it was heard in the farthest corner of the farmyard and all the hens came running together to look at the wonder. Some boasted how white it was, others praised its beautiful shape and others disputed whether it would hatch a pullet or a cockerel. About this the hens

115

often fell into a quarrel so that at last there was such a chattering and cackling, that all the maid had to do, was to go where the noise was in order to be sure of finding the eggs. The old Cockerel was troubled at the loss of the eggs as much as the hens, if not more.

One day after he had been walking up and down thinking, in a corner of the farmyard, he flew upon the edge of the watering trough, shut his eyes and crowed a loud and piercing Cock-a-doodle-doo. At this well known call, the hens came rushing and tumbling from all sides and formed a clucking assembly around the Cockerel. Then he made a very strong speech and told the hens that he knew perfectly well how often they had to mourn over the loss of their eggs and that after long reflection he could think of no better advice than to leave the farmyard and go off into the woods. If they were willing to do this they should get up early the next day. A loud clucking announced their assent to this proposition, and all of them went rather early to roost so that they might get a good sleep before starting. The next morning the Cockerel woke up his wives with a sort of low crowing and they started in perfect silence out of the farmyard. But as the last of the hens left the yard he flew upon the gate and crowed an exulting Cock-a-doodle-doo, and they all went on further and further till they got into the woods.

There they made a great nest in a thicket for their eggs and at night they roosted in the trees. For a while they got on pretty well, only the hens cackled so loudly when they laid their eggs that once the fox heard it and came stealthily up at night and carried off a white brood hen from her nest and smashed the eggs. For the old Cockerel this was a great affliction and after it the hens went about looking quite down-hearted. And when the autumn wind shook

the leaves from the trees and the hens often had to scratch all day without finding a kernel of anything to eat they went to the Cockerel and begged him to lead them back to the farmyard. There they said it was true their eggs were taken away from them, but they had a warm roost and good food; here in the woods the fox broke their eggs and ate them up into the bargain.

The Cockerel, who had himself privately begun to long for the heap of barley-corns, agreed at once to go back, advising the hens for the future to leave off cackling so as not always to betray where the eggs were. But they did not want to take his advice. They said that when they cackled they did it because they knew they had done a good thing; but that he often set up his noise without any reason; at least none of them had ever seen that he had laid an egg.

... The Cockerel led his family back to the farmyard where they fell upon the heap of barley-corns with a very keen appetite. There they live to this very day and have the same sort of food, the same cackling and the same trouble.

See also Animal Farm, Folktales, Foster Mothers

HEN-WIFE

The hen-wife was a woman put in charge of the poultry. In Scotland she held an important post among Highland chiefs. Tenants paid part of their rent in hens – the hen-wife would check and reject hens of an inferior quality and more would have to be brought. At Castle Grant records show that tenants would pay with 20 hens at six monthly intervals.

HOUDAN

The Houdan was originally called the Normandy Fowl and was introduced to England in 1850. It is one of the oldest of the French breeds and was named after the town of Houdan which is west of Paris. Houdans are large, heavy looking birds, bred for the table and have a bold, active character. The head is large and crested with a short beak, leaf type comb and muffled face. The legs are black and like the Faverolles and Dorking, they have a fifth toe. Being a heavy table bird, cocks can weigh in at nearly 4kg. They are fairly good layers of large white eggs. They do tend towards broodiness but are not good sitters as they are too heavy and tend to break the eggs. Houdans are extremely docile in nature and like to be handled especially if they have been raised from young so make good pets. Bantam versions of the large fowl are available.

HOUSING

Chickens need a hen house in which to shelter, roost for the night and lay their eggs. Hen houses come in all shapes, sizes and materials. Most commonly hen houses are wooden, but plastic and metal are also an option. A minimum of 2/3 sq m should be allowed per bird (although suppliers of hen houses often say only 1/3 sq m is necessary). The important factors are that the hutch should be well ventilated and weather proof with a floor and preferably a droppings board. Shavings, sawdust or straw can be used as bedding material but not hay as it can be mouldy and cause respiratory problems. Hutches should be cleaned out every few days; droppings can be used in the compost. Perches should be installed at least 45cm above the ground – big hens need low perches but lighter breeds like to perch higher up. Nest boxes should be

placed in the darkest corner off the ground but below the height of the perches if possible to prevent birds roosting in them at night. Ventilation is important because it prevents a build up of bacteria and condensation. Preferably it should be near the roof. Any windows should be covered with wire mesh. For the roof, felt should not be used as red mite can get under it and cause real problems. Corrugated bituminous Onduline or Coroline roofing sheets fixed onto plyboard are ideal. A pop-hole will let hens in and out of the house – these can close vertically or horizontally but need to be locked against foxes and badgers. Badgers may be able to open vertical doors with their snout. Automatic pop-holes can be purchased and timers set to close at dusk and open in the morning. Hen houses can be static or mobile. A static hen house is best raised off the ground so that hens can shelter underneath – in fact there are hen houses on the market that are raised by just over a metre off the ground and come with a special ladder – these are fox and badger proof. Mobile houses such as arks will come with wheels so they can be manoeuvred to new patches of grass. Chickens can survive really cold weather and sub zero temperatures, such as that experienced in Britain in recent winters as they are homeothermic (warm-blooded). They will seek protection from cold winds by fluffing up their feathers which creates air space between feathers and skin.

See also Bedding, Nest Boxes, Perches, Space

HYBRIDS

There are many hybrids now on the market which have been bred to be specifically good at egg laying but after two years of intensive laying, production of eggs will decrease. Hybrids were originally

119

developed for intensive production and kept in battery conditions – the brown egg layers were based on the Rhode Island Red and have trade names such as Shaver and ISA Brown. Isa Warrens, also known as Rangers, are brown-feathered hybrids that have been specifically bred for free range. Recently other hybrids have also been developed for free range conditions and to look attractive in the garden. One of the most successful is the Black Rock (see separate entry). There are many other hybrids on the market. Calder Rangers (also known as Columbian Blacktails and used by Waitrose for their free range eggs) are consistently good layers as are White Stars (developed from Leghorns and layers of white eggs). Bovans Nera, Hebden Black and the Speckledy are all successful hybrids and more recently the Rhode Rock (Rhode Island Red crossed with barred Plymouth Rock has come on the market). Meadowsweet Poultry Services have agents across the country and their range includes Black Star (same as Rhode Rock), Bluebelle (a Marans and Rhode Island Red cross) and Speckled Star (French Marans hybrid similar to the Speckledy). All these hens lay between 220 and 320 eggs a year. There is another group of poultry suppliers selling a relatively newly named group of hybrids – they have names such as Fenning Black and Fenning White, Mendlesham or Fenning Blue (similar to Bluebelle), Fenning Coucou (French Marans hybrid), Suffolk Blacktail (a Rhode Island Red hybrid), Suffolk Noir (a black Copper Marans hybrid) and Pied Suffolk. Other names for hybrids (all based on Rhode Island Red, Sussex, Marans and Leghorn) include Coral Nova, Amber Nova or Star, Blue Nova (similar to Bluebelle), Cuckoo Nova (from Cuckoo Marans), Sussex Nova, Silver Nova and Columbine (blue egg layer).

I

INCUBATORS AND ARTIFICIAL INCUBATING

The Egyptians used their own incubators to hatch thousands of chicks, an amazingly advanced technological process for the time. Egypt had a mass society and a large labour force building the pyramids and therefore needed a lot of food. The Egyptians built their incubators of clay brick in which fires were kept burning by a slave who managed to maintain the fires at a temperature necessary for incubation – this is around 37.5°C. These structures were used to hatch the chicks and acted as brooders as well to keep the chicks warm until ready to fend for themselves. The fact that the Egyptians were mass producing poultry means they must have also mastered procedures for caring for large flocks, collecting and distributing eggs and must have used the birds for meat. China may well have also mastered the art of incubation in order to feed the workers who built the Great Wall of China. Later on in their history the Chinese used the heat of manure heaps to incubate eggs.

It was not until 1881 that a hatching-machine in which the heat could be regulated was invented by Charles Hearson and used in Europe. These machines were heated by oil lamps and held up to 200 eggs. In America Lyman Byce is credited with the invention of an egg incubator in 1879.

Modern manual and automatic incubators come in all sorts of sizes. Manufacturers' instructions must be followed closely as varying results can be achieved from identical incubators, which proves that it all depends on the person operating the system. Most

incubators turn eggs automatically which are stored on their sides. Eggs should be candled at 10 days and infertile eggs removed. Moisture is important and 55% should be the relative humidity, going up to 65% for the last three days. A temperature of 37.8°C should be maintained.

INDIAN GAME
Indian Game were for many years bred in Cornwall and were called Cornish Game. Bred mainly for meat consumption this breed is big breasted and hens are poor layers. Asils, Old English Game and Malays were used to develop the breed.

INFECTIOUS BRONCHITIS
The symptoms for this viral respiratory infection are sneezing, gasping and a watery discharge from mouth and nostrils. There is no treatment; birds should recover but a decrease in egg production is to be expected and the oviduct may be damaged resulting in a future of soft-shelled eggs.

ITALIAN BREEDS Named after places
Both the Ancona and Leghorn were named after cities in Italy. Ancona is located on the Adriatic coast. The Leghorn was named after Leghorn, now Livorno, which is a port on the Ligurian Sea in the north west of Italy.
See separate entries under individual breeds

IXWORTH
The Ixworth breed was created by Mr Appleyard in 1932 and was named after a village in Suffolk. Various breeds were used in its development including all white birds from Sussex, Orpington, Minorca and Indian Game. The Ixworth is white and available in large and bantam size. It is a rare breed and lays tinted eggs.

J

JAPANESE BANTAM

These are true bantams from
Japan developed uniquely
and come in three types of
feathering – silkie, frizzle
or normal and in various
colours, but most commonly
black-tailed white or mottled.
They are very squat with the
shortest legs of any breed so it is difficult to tell whether a bantam
is sitting or standing. Japanese Bantams have a long upright tail
with their wings carried low. Hens lay white eggs.

JERSEY GIANT

Originating in New Jersey in America from Brahmas, Langshans
and Indian Game, the large fowl are giants! Available in white,
black or blue, hens lay brown eggs and there are bantam versions.

JUNGLE FOWL

The progenitor of today's domestic chicken is generally thought to
be the Red Jungle Fowl (Gallus Bankiva or Ferrugineus) – this
resembles the game breeds and origination ranged from India to
the East Indies and Philippines. There are three other wild species
which are all Asian – the Grey Jungle Fowl (Gallus Sonnerati) is
native to India; Lafayette's Jungle Fowl (Gallus Lafayettii) native
to Sri Lanka and Gallus Furcatus from Java.

K

KELLOGG'S CORN FLAKES
THE RED AND GREEN ROOSTER

Dr John Harvey Kellogg was an American who, with his brother, invented corn flakes. While developing the brand he gave up selling the cereal in sacks and started using boxes. He needed a logo for his Kellogg's Corn Flakes. His friend, Nancy Richards, was a Welsh harpist and suggested that Kellogg was similar to the name for a cockerel in Welsh – Ceiliog – and that therefore the logo should be a rooster. The cockerel is of course the herald of dawn and, by extension, breakfast. It is thought that the rooster was made red and green for Ddraig Goch, the Red Dragon of Wales.

KRAIENKÖPPE (Dutch = TWENTSE)
A rare breed originating on the border between Germany and Holland, hens lay white eggs and bantams are available.

L

LA FLÈCHE

This is a French table breed, black in colour with a horn comb. Hens lay tinted eggs and there is a bantam version.

LAKENVELDER

It is unclear whether this breed originated in the Netherlands or Germany. The Dutch claim the Lakenvelder was named after the village of Lakenvelt. Others think that the name came from Lakenvel, meaning shadow on a sheet and still others say the breed was named after Lakenvelder cattle which have black heads and tails and white over the rest of their bodies. It is also generally believed that the breed originated in the Westphalian area of Germany. Lakenvelders are striking with their white feathered long bodies contrasting with black neck and tail feathers; this colour marking is called belted. They lay white eggs, are non-sitters and flighty, not liking to be cooped up. Large fowl and bantams are available.

LANGSHAN

There are three types of Langshan, the Modern, Croad and German. The Modern Langshan is a separate taller breed which was developed for showing but is now very rare. The Croad Langshan is an old heavy, soft-feathered breed which may have originated in China. The breed was first imported to Britain in 1872 by Major Croad. The original Croad Langshans were black with a brilliant green sheen and this is the most popular colour although white is an alternative colour. The Croad Langshan is large with slightly feathered legs. Hens lay brown eggs and are good sitters and mothers. The German version also came from China but differs in that it is clean-legged. The Langshan has been used in the development of breeds such as Barnevelders, Black Orpingtons and Maranses. Large fowl and bantams are available.

LAWRENCE, DH

DH Lawrence spent some of his time during his last years on his ranch in New Mexico where he kept a favourite cow as well as his cockerel and hens. In an essay, '*Aristocracy*', Lawrence describes his white cock Moses: 'And as the white cock calls in the doorway,

who calls? Merely a barnyard rooster, worth a dollar-and-a-half. But listen! Under the old dawns of creation the Holy Ghost, the Mediator, shouts aloud in the twilight. And every time I hear him, a fountain of vitality gushes up in my body. It is life.'

Despite seeming to enjoy keeping poultry, DH Lawrence was known for his cruelty to animals – he chopped off the head of one of his hens because he couldn't stop it being broody despite having hung it upside down for several days 'to cool it underneath'.
See *The Escaped Cock* and *Cocksure Women and Hensure Men*

LAYING EGGS See Egg Laying, Point of Lay

LAYING HENS, BEHAVIOUR OF
Hens, especially, pullets about to lay for the first time, may take a day searching out a nest site, visiting and investigating several potential spots before choosing one. They may spend some time preparing the nest, moving straw or similar with their beaks and hollowing out the spot. If a cockerel is present he may get involved, helping to suggest and preparing sites himself. Once a hen starts laying, she will also exhibit pre-laying behaviour about an hour before her egg is actually laid. She may, for example, queue up to lay in a popular nest box that is already being used, as hens quite like to use the same nest box. Alternatively she may visit several suitable sites, sit for a bit and then change her mind until laying reasonably quickly in the first place that she chose. Sometimes hens can be caught short and lay their eggs on the ground while going about other activities!
See also Egg Laying, Nesting

LEGHORN

The Leghorn is an important and popular breed which originated from the Port of Leghorn (now Livorno) in Italy and was imported into Britain in the late 1800s, with white first and then brown birds. Leghorns have had the longest life of any of the productive breeds ever introduced. There is evidence from old pictures that this type of bird with a flop-over comb in the female was to be found in many countries of Europe. Old breeds such as the Belgian Brakel, Pheasant Fowls and the Scots Grey had similar features such as white earlobes, flop-over combs and laid white eggs. It is possible therefore that this Mediterranean type was the original fowl of Europe and that the heavier type of Leghorn evident today was due to crossing Malays, Cochins and Minorcas. Prolific layers of white eggs, Leghorns are a light, soft-feathered breed and non-sitters. There are now other colour variations available such as black, barred, buff, cuckoo, mottled, exchequer and partridge, and bantams are miniatures of their large fowl counterparts.
See Brown Eggs versus White Eggs

LICE

Poultry can easily attract lice, which are irritating for the bird and in fact dust bathing helps them to rid themselves of lice and other bugs. Birds can be treated with louse powder. The nest boxes and dust baths can also be dusted with powder as can broody hens before sitting.

LIGHT AND LIGHTING

Light is very important to hens and the hours of daylight will determine when a hen comes into lay. As the days get longer she will lay well but as the days begin to shorten in late summer/early autumn she will stop laying, moult and if she is a pure breed will probably not start laying again until end of January/February when the days start to lengthen again. Hens possess a complex mechanism – a small organ behind the eye is influenced by the amount of light in the day and sends messages to the ovary which affect the ovulation process. Commercial breeders use artificial light to keep hens laying all year round. Lighting can be fixed in hen houses, with a timer, in winter but should be used to provide extra light for two or three hours before dawn rather than in the evening, to allow hens to roost naturally.

LIGHT BREEDS

Light Breeds are traditionally those with a good reputation for egg laying, rather than as table birds. Usually, they will lay good numbers of white or cream eggs but sometimes have a tendency to be flighty, so regular and careful handling is beneficial. Light breeds include Ancona, Minorca, Leghorn, Poland, Hamburgh and Silkie. Also classed as light breeds are Welsummer and Araucana despite laying brown and blue eggs respectively.

LINCOLNSHIRE BUFF

The Lincolnshire Buff was a dual purpose utility breed found not surprisingly in Lincolnshire. During the 1800s and early 1900s, it was supplied to London markets as a white fleshed table bird and was widely sold as a good winter layer. Standardisation of the Buff Orpington, which many at the time considered to be a refined Lincolnshire Buff, led to its demise in the 1920s, although its genetic material lived on in the Orpington. In the 1980s the breed was re-developed using the Orpington with the Cochin and Dorking. This produced an ideal laying hen. The Lincolnshire looks similar to the Orpington but carries its tail lower, has a longer back and tighter feathering – it is also one of the few five-toed breeds.

LITTLE RED HEN see Hen Tales for Children

 LITTLE RED ROOSTER

I am the Little Red Rooster was a Rolling Stones song recorded in 1964: 'I am the little red rooster, too lazy to crow for day … little red rooster's on the prowl. If you see my little red rooster, please drive him home … Ain't had no peace in the farmyard, since my little red rooster's gone'.

 LOVE AMONG THE CHICKENS by PG Wodehouse

Love Among the Chickens (written in 1906) is a humorous novel about an irrepressible entrepreneur, Stanley Featherstonehaugh Ukridge, who sets up a chicken farm in Dorset and involves his friend Jeremy Garnet. The novel intertwines Garnet's love affair with a local girl and the vicissitudes of making a living from keeping hens and selling eggs.

M

MALAY

The Malay is an old hard-feathered breed, originating in Asia, which came to Britain about 1830. Malays are very upright with long necks and legs which gives them an elegant stance. They have been used in the creation of many large poultry breeds but they were also the first breed to be developed as bantams. Hens lay only a small number of tinted eggs over the spring and summer.

MANURE

Poultry manure is an extremely valuable fertiliser. It can be added to the compost heap as an activator – it is full of nitrogen. Fresh poultry manure is generally regarded as too strong to go straight onto vegetable plots. It can be applied directly to comfrey. It can also be put round blackcurrant bushes as they love nitrogen. Droppings in a water butt produce excellent liquid feed. One hen produces about 5½kg of manure a year. Moisture content is about 60% and this is why it needs to be dried. It also contains too much nitrogen so in order to use it as a complete manure, bone meal and potash need to be added. To every 12kg of manure, 3kg of bone meal and 150g of sulphate of potash need to be added. An alternative would be to use the dried poultry manure as a nitrogenous fertiliser and apply along rows of brassicas that need extra nitrogen. A good way of using poultry manure is to dry the droppings as quickly as possible spreading them out on metal trays in a shed and then

pulverizing them possibly with the back of a spade. Poultry manure can also be effective with just potash added (bonfire ash from a wood fire is ideal).

MARANS

English ships sailing into Marans in France, near La Rochelle, in the 1800s used to carry hens and fighting cocks. These were exchanged with fresh hens from Marans and the region became the birthplace of a particular breed of poultry, originally called the Marandaise, later to become the Marans. Around 1880 two brothers, poultry merchants from London, were responsible for spreading knowledge of the Marans hens. One of them was a wholesaler of white Russian eggs (Russia was at this time an important poultry producing country). The other brother, whose ships docked at Marans, had the idea of competing with the white Russian egg trade by selling the dark brown eggs of Marans hens which were bigger and fresher. Thus the eggs soon became popular in the London markets. Maranses were crossed with Brahmas and Langshans in order to make the eggs browner – Brahmas were used for their egg laying abilities and the Langshans for the dark brown colour of their eggs.

Maranses weren't introduced to Britain until 1929 – there are two types – French and English. The English are cuckoo and clean legged (they look similar to barred Plymouth Rocks) and the French can be wheaten, copper black, black, white or Columbian and have feathered legs. Classed as a heavy breed, the Marans is the one pure breed where it is relatively easy to distinguish male and female chicks – males have a white spot on the top of their heads while females have a darker one. They are a good choice of breed for free range as they are good foragers. Bantams are available as miniatures of their large fowl counterpart. The Marans' eggs are so special that in France competitions are held on the size, shape, texture and dark colour of the eggs. The colour ranges from brown to a dark chocolate colour. Bantams are usually not that tame and not particularly keen on being touched. They can be unreliable layers but do go broody and are worth keeping just for the colour of the eggs.

MAREK'S DISEASE

This is a common virus that causes tumours – clinical signs include paralysis of legs, wings and neck; loss of weight; grey iris or irregular pupil; vision impairment; and the skin around feather follicles can be raised and roughened. The disease was first recognised by the Hungarian vet Jozsef Marek in 1907 and was at one time the most common cause of losses in the poultry industry. It is now largely controlled by the use of vaccines. It usually affects birds between five and 25 weeks of age. It is a highly contagious disease that may survive for months or years in litter and poultry dust. Infection occurs through the respiratory tract and infected birds can remain carriers long after infection. There is no treatment.

MARKET/POULTRY AUCTION

Poultry auctions take place, often as part of livestock markets across the country. This is probably not the best place for beginners to obtain their chickens. Breeders never send their best hens and cockerels to market. Stories abound of people bidding for four hens for example and when they get them home they eventually find they have four cockerels!

MARSH DAISY

The Marsh Daisy is a rare breed created in the 1880s in Southport, Lancashire where Old English Game roosters were crossed with Malay hens to create the foundation for the breed. Black Hamburghs, White Leghorns and Sicilian Buttercups were also added to cement its characteristics. Its name may be related to its origin in a marsh-like area, or it may be that its large rose comb resembles the flower of the Marsh Daisy. The Marsh Daisy is hardy and slow to mature. It is a lightweight breed, a good forager and does well as a free ranger. Though generally calm, it is active and can fly. Hens lay tinted eggs. The only colours available now are brown or wheaten. No bantams have been developed in this breed.

MEAT CHICKENS

Meat chickens, also known as broilers, are especially bred for meat. The most intensively farmed chickens are killed at six weeks, the free range are killed at 8 weeks and organic at 12 weeks. Chicks reared naturally by a mother hen are often still sheltering under her wing at six weeks! Broilers are kept in massive sheds with 19 birds per square metre. There is no natural light and their short lives are spent with nothing to do but eat, drink and defecate.

The litter on the floor absorbs droppings but the air becomes terribly polluted by ammonia which can damage the chickens' eyes, respiratory system and burn their legs and feet (known as hock burns and seen as red marks on raw chicken legs). Leg deformities occur because chickens are unable to support their increased, unnatural body weight and this weight also puts pressure on their hearts and lungs. Many chickens die in the sheds from heart failure.

MIKE-THE-HEADLESS-CHICKEN (Also known as THE HEADLESS WONDER CHICKEN)

In 1945 a Wyandotte rooster was living in a backyard in Fruita, Colorado. Mr Olsen was sent out to kill the rooster for dinner. He used an axe to behead the cockerel but the execution did not quite go according to plan. The rooster staggered around but did not die. The next morning the rooster, Mike, was still alive and Mr Olsen decided to work out a way to feed and water him. He used an eyedropper to give him grain and water. He then took the cockerel to the University of Utah and was told that the axe had missed the jugular vein and a clot had prevented Mike from bleeding to death. Although most of his head was now missing, most of his brain stem and one ear had been left on his body. Mike lived for 18 months, growing in size and weight to about 4 kg, was taken on tour and people paid to see him. Then one night Mike started choking, and Olsen did not have his eyedropper to clear his oesophagus, so was unable to save him. Mike's life is still celebrated in an annual festival held in May in Fruita.

MINORCA

The Minorca probably originated in Spain and used to be very popular since the hen was a prolific layer of very large white eggs. Minorcas have large white earlobes which look rather out of proportion. They are a light soft-feathered breed and can be black or white. The hen has a large single comb which drops down over her face. Bantams are available. The hens in *Animal Farm* were Minorcas.

MODERN GAME

The Modern Game breed was developed in England from the Old English Game in the 1850s, after the outlawing of cockfighting and the development of exhibition as a new and popular sport. These birds have very long legs and neck, a tiny tail and a compact body. The males were dubbed (comb, wattles and lobes trimmed) upon reaching adulthood, resulting in a streamlined, elegant head. Hens have a small straight comb. Colours are dramatic and varied, including: black-breasted red, blue-breasted red, silver duckwing, golden duckwing, birchen, brown red, pyle, lemon blue, silver blue, blue, black, and white.

MOULTING

The natural moulting time is late summer or early autumn. Most hens will stop laying then and cocks will stop mating. Occasionally a hen will go on laying while moulting and a few may resume laying while moulting is still in progress. Moulting usually lasts between eight and 12 weeks. Feathers are lost from the head and neck first, then from the saddle, breast and body, then the wings and lastly from the tail; scales from the skin, looking like large bits of dandruff, may be evident on the droppings board. Hens born in the spring and summer will not usually moult until the autumn of the next year. Usually it is the poor egg layers that moult early and the better the layer, the later in the year she will moult. Pin feathers may be seen – these are the new emerging feathers and usually indicate a short moult. The scales on the legs also moult every year. The cockerel will have a partial moult losing and replacing mainly his neck and tail feathers. During this process he will be infertile as his energy will be used to replace feathers.

MUFFLING

Muffling is all the feathering on the face including the beard and whiskers but not including the crest. Muffling can be seen on Faverolles and the Houdan.

MYCOPLASMA

This is a respiratory infection which starts with sneezing and coughing, a runny nose and eyes, and sometimes a rasping noise in the affected bird's breathing can be heard. It can be treated with an injection of Tylan 200.

N

NANKIN

The Nankin is a true bantam and is about the same size as a Sebright. According to H Easom Smith, Nankins were probably used in the development of the Sebrights, showing that the breed has been around for a very long time. There is a lot of speculation as to where they came from but they were most likely to have been introduced to Britain from India. The name, however, originates from Nankeen which is a buff-coloured cotton cloth first made at Nanking in China. The Nankin is a hardy bird that is slow to mature and lays a tiny creamy white egg. The hens make excellent brooders and protective mothers. Nankins are able to tolerate being kept in confinement although they can be flighty. The body of a Nankin is a buff colour with black tail feathers. The comb can be either single or rose.

NESTING AND NEST BOXES

Nest boxes are essential for laying hens and should be a minimum of 40cm wide, 30cm deep and 40 cm high. One nest is needed for every four birds although often hens share the same nest box. Nest boxes, which can be wooden or plastic, should be bedded down with shavings, sawdust or straw and have a lip to prevent eggs rolling out. Free range hens will most likely find their own nesting spots which will be dry, dark, cosy and hidden away – they may be in undergrowth or high on a shelf in a shed, for example or in a

pot of compost, behind an oil tank, in a sage bush or even in the grass collector of a mower.

NEW HAMPSHIRE RED

This breed originated in 1915 in the US where it was bred from the Rhode Island Red in New Hampshire although the birds are very different in colouring and body shape from the original Rhode Island Red. These birds were originally bred for the eggs. The body of a New Hampshire Red is well rounded with a deep full breast and medium length tail. The head is deep and rather flat on top with prominent eyes, a single comb, large wattles and red earlobes. The legs are yellow and the feathers are a deep chestnut red. The chicks are quick to feather up and mature. Birds thrive in a run or wandering free and as they are not good fliers, they do not need particularly high fencing. They do not tend to go broody and are good layers of brown eggs. Large fowl and bantams are available.

NEW HENS ADDED TO AN ESTABLISHED FLOCK

When increasing the flock two or more hens should be added at any one time. New hens should be kept separate from the established flock for a few days. If there is no alternative they can be put into the hen house at night when all is quiet. Spraying all the hens with a little water to which a few drops of vinegar have been added is one idea – chickens have a reasonable sense of smell so if they all smell the same, this can help new hens to be accepted.

NON-SITTERS

Non-sitters are hens that do not go broody since their maternal instincts have been practically suspended. This comes about in

breeds where the good layers have been selectively bred, and is how the modern hybrids have been developed. Most of the pure breed non-sitters lay white shelled eggs and are light breeds. They include: Ancona, Andalusian, Campine, Hamburgh, Lakenfelder, Leghorn, Minorca, Poland, Redcap, Scots Grey and Transylvanian Naked Neck. Welsummers although layers of brown eggs and are also meant to be non-sitters but can sometimes go broody.

NORFOLK GREY

The Norfolk Grey originates from the town of Norwich. The breed was created by Fred Myhill before the First World War as utility birds under the name Black Marias. The name was reminiscent of funerals and was quickly dropped and the breed took the name Norfolk Grey instead. The breed was first exhibited at the Dairy Show in 1920 classed as a heavy breed but they are not actually that large and only weigh around 3 - 4kg. They were developed by crossing birchen English Game with duckwing Leghorns. Hens are black in colour with silver lacing on the neck and cockerels a mixture of silver and black – they have single combs and black legs. The Norfolk Grey is a rare breed which almost disappeared in the early 1970s but fortunately a private flock was found to contain four birds in 1974 and the breed was revived. There is also a bantam version. The Norfolk Grey does well as a free ranger. Hens lay tinted eggs.

NORTH HOLLAND BLUE

A rare, heavy breed from Holland available in cuckoo colour with feathered legs in large fowl or bantam size. Hens lay tinted eggs.

 **NURSERY RHYMES**

Here are some popular rhymes featuring hens and cockerels:

Hickety, pickety, my black hen,
She lays eggs for gentlemen;
Gentlemen come every day
To see what my black hen doth lay.
Sometimes nine and sometimes ten,
Hickety, pickety, my black hen.

I had a little hen/The prettiest ever seen;
She washed up the dishes/And kept the house clean.
She went to the mill/To fetch me some flour,
And always got home/In less than an hour.
She baked me my bread/She brewed me my ale,
She sat by the fire and told a fine tale.

Chook, chook, chook, chook, chook,
Good morning, Mrs Hen
How many chickens have you got?
Madam, I've got ten.
Four of them are yellow,
And four of them are brown,
The nicest in the town.
Chook, chook, chook, chook, chook,
Cock-a-doodle-doo.

Little Blue Ben, who lives in the glen,
Keeps a blue cat and one blue hen,
Which lays of blue eggs a score and ten;
Where shall I find the Little Blue Ben?

The Cock crows in the morn/To tell us to rise
And he that lies late/Will never be wise;
For early to bed/And early to rise,
Is the way to be healthy /And wealthy and wise.

The Cock's on the wood pile a-blowing his horn,
The bull's in the barn a-threshing of corn,
The maids in the meadows are making of hay,
The ducks in the river are swimming away.

A Russian Nursery Rhyme - The Speckled Hen

This nursery rhyme was adapted by Harve Zemach. It repeats
itself with each verse getting longer. In the last verse the mother
rushes to her husband:

'Wonder of wonders!
At grandmother's house
A little specked hen laid a speckled egg.
Grandmother put it in a little wooden keg.
But out it jumped all by itself
And rolled right off the end of the shelf,
On to the table and down to the floor,
Cracked its shell and was no more!
Then grandmother cried,

142

And grandfather sighed,
The stove poured out smoke,
The window panes broke,
The white geese scattered,
And the fence posts clattered
And then our daughter/Spilled all the water.
And I, your wife, while milking the goat,
Fell off the stool and got mud on my coat!'
Her husband trembled, her husband shook,
And over his face came a terrible look.
His moustache quivered, his ears turned red,
He climbed up a haystack and stood on his head.
'Come down!' cried his wife. 'I dare not,' he said.
'Until the specked hen/Lays a speckled egg again,
Stand here I must and stand here I will!'
So he stood there all night, and he's standing there still.
Wonder of wonders!

The Cock and the Hen

Cock, cock, cock, cock/I've laid an egg
Am I to go ba-are-foot?
Hen, hen, hen, hen/I've been up and down
To every shop in town/And cannot find a shoe
To fit your foot/if I'd crow my hea-art out.

O

OLD ENGLISH GAME

There are two varieties of Old English Game, Carlisle and Oxford, both large fowl. In general these Old Game varieties were used for cockfighting probably from Roman times right up until 1849 when cockfighting became illegal. After this many breeders began to exhibit Game Fowl which have been bred in a multitude of colours. Carlisle and Oxford Old English Game are a hard-feathered breed, tall and slim with long legs. Old English Game Bantams are a recent creation – they are small, laying cream-coloured eggs but are used more as show birds than for their egg-laying abilities. These game breeds are not ideal for the garden – the cockerels can be vicious. Rumpless Game were created in a genetic accident from Old English Game and are available in a bantam version.

OLD ENGLISH PHEASANT FOWL

This is an old breed, now rare, originally called Yorkshire or Golden Pheasant but renamed in 1914. It is a light breed, in large fowl or bantam size, with gold or silver colouring and a rose comb. These birds like to free range and roost in trees. Hens lay white eggs and make reasonable mothers.

ORLOFF

This breed originated in northern Iran and was brought to Moscow where it was renamed after Count Orloff Techesmensky. From Russia Orloffs were imported into Britain, Germany and the Neth-

erlands and an Orloff Club was set up in Britain in the 1920s for
large fowl and bantams. The breed probably originated from game
fowl and has a similar appearance. Originally only in black they
now come in cuckoo, mahogany, white and spangled. Hens lay
tinted eggs.

ORPINGTON

Orpington fowl were named after a village in Kent where William
Cook first bred them in the late 1800s. Langshans, Minorcas and
Plymouth Rocks were involved in its creation and today they still
look similar to the Langshan. The black variety was followed by
the white and then the buff. There is now a blue variety as well.
Orpingtons are compact with short legs and classified as a heavy
soft-feathered breed. Bantams are also available and are very
popular as they are docile and good with children. The Jubilee
Orpington was created in 1897 to commemorate Queen Victoria's
Diamond Jubilee. The Queen Mother used to keep large fowl Buff
Orpingtons. The Large Fowl are big, heavy and rather broad with
an abundance of feathers which makes them look even bigger.
They make good mothers and can sit on a large number of eggs.

They do not fly because of their weight and also have relatively small wings in comparison to their size so are easily kept within the garden; they are docile and good for first time poultry keepers. They lay well and their eggs are light brown but rather small for the size of hen. The village of Orpington boasts a pub called The Buff with a sign displaying a Buff Orpington cockerel.

OVIDUCT

A long tube-like organ in the laying hen which accepts the yolk after ovulation and down which the egg will pass as it forms and becomes surrounded by its albumen and shell.

OYSTERSHELLS see Feeding

P

PACE EGGS

Pace-egging is an ancient Lancashire custom once widespread, and is still to be found in parts of the county today. Pace derives from Paschal, the old name for Easter. Pace-Eggs are hard-boiled eggs, traditionally decorated for Easter. The eggs are first wrapped in onion skins and boiled, giving the shells a golden, mottled effect; or they can be boiled and then painted.

At the Wordsworth Museum in Grasmere a collection of highly decorated eggs originally made for the poet's children is exhibited. Usually Pace-eggs were either eaten on Easter Sunday or handed out to the Pace-eggers. These Pace-eggers were once a common sight in Lancashire villages. They were fantastically dressed Mummers complete with blackened faces, who toured the villages enacting the Pace-egging Play. This was a drama with the characters of St George, Old Tosspot and a battle. The Pace-egger's song would also be sung.

Pace-egg Rolling is another old custom. In Avenham Park in Preston the crowds still gather every year on Easter Monday to watch the traditional egg-rolling contest down the grassy slopes. The eggs are hard-boiled and then decorated, and hundreds of children compete to see whose egg can roll the furthest without cracking. These are also called Egg-specking Contests or Easter Egg Rolls and are held at The White House in the US every year.

PATHE COCKEREL LOGO

The Pathe cockerel logo was originally a red rooster when Charles Pathe set up the film company in 1890. In the cinema the logo was presented with a cock crowing at full volume at the beginning of all Pathe films. Pathe was eventually absorbed by Warner Brothers but in 1995 a new company British-Pathe was set up with a new

logo – a white cockerel sits on a surrounding wreath with the emblems of England, Scotland, Wales and Ireland. The crowing was not copyrighted to Pathe and stopped 30 years ago.

PECKING ORDER

A cockerel looking after a group of hens will be at the top of the pecking order. Hens under him will fight to be the second most powerful by pecking each other. If a hen loses a fight she will adopt a subservient pose, with her body lowered and legs bent. Incidentally, the larger a hen's comb is, the more she will be feared by others and she will probably automatically gain second place in the pecking order. If there is no cockerel in the group, the hen with the largest comb will probably be boss and will take on a male role – she may even crow! New hens introduced to an established group may take a while to achieve a pecking order – on the whole older hens will be more self-confident and expect a high rank while younger, more timid hens may go straight to the bottom of the pecking order. If there are two cocks, one will become dominant, or they may fight, especially if they are enclosed, and have to be separated. Hens often develop friendships just like humans – sometimes two or three hens will stick together during the day and at night.

See also Crowing Hens, New Hens

PEEP OF CHICKENS

The collective term for a group of chickens.

PEKIN BANTAM

The Pekin was introduced to Britain from China. In 1860 the summer palace of the Chinese Emperor at Pekin was sacked by English and French forces and some Pekin bantams were brought home to England as plunder. The Pekin was originally thought to be a miniature of the Cochin, but in reality has no connection with it. Pekins are a genuine bantam breed and are small with feathered feet and are a wonderful tame breed for children. They are popular as they look round and cuddly. They come in a variety of colours including black, blue, buff, white, cuckoo, lavender and partridge. They don't lay particularly well and the eggs are small, being light beige. The hens go broody frequently and can be very persistent about remaining broody. Their disadvantage is that the feathered feet tend to get wet and muddy very easily. However the advantage is they won't scratch up the garden as they are hindered by their feathered feet. They will need dry conditions for perching so that their leg feathers can dry. The advantage of keeping Pekin cockerels is they crow quite softly.

PERCHES AND PERCHING

Chickens like to sleep on perches at night but also like to perch during the day on low branches or on top of hutches or runs especially if it is wet. Perches should not be too high because even

if the birds can fly up to them, they may not find it so easy to fly down and may get bumblefoot (see separate entry). They can be fitted as low as 30cm so that heavy breeds such as Orpingtons can manage to get up to them. Perches should be about 4 – 5cm wide and made from smooth wood, bevelled either side and each bird will need at least 20cm of space. Perches can be either positioned at the same level or at different levels but birds may fight for positions on the highest perch. Chickens do not fall off perches when they are asleep – their legs are designed so that the toes automatically clench when bent (a kind of locking mechanism) and so toes will wrap around the perch as they sit down.

PETALUMA

Petaluma, a city in California, used to be known as the Egg Capital of the World. It developed huge grain milling and chicken processing industries and this caused such nicknames as Chickaluma. Petaluma hosted the only known poultry drugstore and is the place where the first practical egg incubator was invented by Lyman Byce in 1879. In fact one of the largest historic chicken processing plants still stands in the central area of town although this 1930s brick building is no longer used for the chicken industry.

PIPPING

Pipping is the technical term used for the chick breaking out of the shell when it hatches.

PLYMOUTH ROCK

The well known variety is the barred Plymouth Rock (the 'barred' refers to the markings) but this breed is also popular in white and

buff. It was developed in New England in the early 1800s from crosses of Dominiques, Black Javas and Cochins and first exhibited in 1869; they are still popular in the US.

The Plymouth Rock was named by its founder DJC Bennett in honour of America's founding pilgrims who disembarked from their ship, The Mayflower, at Plymouth Rock (Massachusetts) in 1620. (The boulder on which they supposedly landed has now been moved and is housed at Pilgrim Memorial State Park in Massachusetts). The Plymouth Rock is a heavy dual purpose breed, available as large fowl or bantam, and hens are excellent layers of tinted eggs. They are used in the development of the autosexing breeds as well as hybrids such as the Black Rock and Rhode Rock.

 POEMS

Here are some well loved poems featuring hens and cockerels:

The Hen by Christina Rossetti
A white hen sitting
On white eggs three;
Next, three speckled chickens
As plump as plump can be.
An owl and a hawk
And a bat come to see;
But chicks beneath their mother's wing
Squat safe as safe can be.

The Browny Hen by Irene F Fawsey

A browny hen sat on her nest
With a hey-ho for the springtime!
Seven brown eggs 'neath her downy breast,
With a hey-ho for the springtime!
A brown hen clucks all day from dawn,
With a hey-ho for the springtime!
She's seven wee chicks as yellow as corn,
With a hey-ho for the springtime!

From *The Beggar's Opera* by Jon Gay (1728)

Before the barn door crowing
The cock by hens attended
Stands for a while suspended;
Then one he singles from the crew,
And cheers the happy hen,
With how do you do and how do you do,
And how do you do again.

Five Little Chickens - Anon

Said the first little chicken/With a queer little squirm,
'Oh I wish I could find /A fat little worm!'

Said the second little chicken/With a small sigh of grief,
'Oh I wish I could find/A little green leaf!'

Said the third little chicken/With a sharp little squeal,
'Oh I wish I could find/Some nice yellow meal!'

Said the fourth little chicken/With a small sigh of grief,
'Oh, I wish I could find/A green little leaf!'

Said the fifth little chicken/With a faint little moan,
'Oh I wish I could find/A wee gravel stone!'

'Now see here,' said their mother/From the green garden patch,
'If you want any breakfast/You must all come and scratch!'

The Clucking Hen by A Hawkshawe

Pray will you take a walk with me,
My little wife, today?
There's barley in the barley fields,
And hay seeds in the hay.

Thank you, said the clucking hen,
I've something else to do.
I'm busy sitting on my eggs;
I cannot walk with you.

The clucking hen sat on her nest,
She made it in the hay;
And warm and snug beneath her breast,
A dozen white eggs lay.

Crack crack, went all the little eggs,
Cheep cheep the chickens small!
Cluck! Said the clucking hen,
Now I have you all.

Now come along, my little chicks
I'll take a walk with YOU.
Hello then crowed the barn-door cock,
And cockadoodle doo!

Cock-crow by Edward Thomas

Out of the wood of thoughts that grows by night
To be cut down by the sharp axe of light,
Out of the night, two cocks together crow,
Cleaving the darkness with a silver blow:
And bright before my eyes twin trumpeters stand,
Heralds of splendour, one at either hand,
Each facing each as in a coat of arms:
The milkers lace their boots up at the farms.

POINT OF LAY

Hens start laying eggs between the ages of 18 and 22 weeks and
this is known as Point of Lay (POL). Hybrids are usually sold at
this age and will start laying regardless of the time of year. For pure
breeds the time of year is more important. POL will depend on
when they hatched. If they have been born in February for example
then they may start laying in July. If the days are shortening when
they reach sexual maturity then they may not start laying until the
following spring.

An easy pointer to a hen that is laying is a red comb which is
warm to the touch. Her tail will be also be erect. On a more technical
basis, the distance between the pelvic bones can be measured and
should be about 5cm or the width of three fingers apart. The
distance between the end of the breastbone and the pelvic bones
can also be assessed – if a hen is laying, there should be a width of
four fingers. When a hen stops laying, her comb will be pale and
the vent (the opening between the pelvic bones) will close to one
finger's width. Beak pigment in yellow skinned breeds such as
Leghorns, Wyandottes and Rhode Island Reds can help in deciding

if a hen is laying. When a hen starts laying her beak will be full of pigment (look yellow) as will her legs and feet.

See Beak Pigment

POLAND

The Crested Dutch or Polish breed was imported from eastern Europe and in England renamed Poland. The Poland has a long history going back to the 16th Century. It is an ornamental breed available as large fowl and bantam with hens being non-sitters and laying white eggs. The most striking feature is the crest of feathers on top of its head – the most popular variety is the white-crested black Poland. Polands are very flighty and are scared easily – this could be because they find it difficult to see as the crest partially covers their eyes. It is recommended that some of the feathers round their eyes are trimmed. There is a new variety the Frizzled Poland adopted from Holland.

PORTUGUESE COCKEREL – THE LEGEND OF THE BARCELOS COCKEREL

The cockerel is the national emblem in Portugal and is seen everywhere decorating pottery and souvenirs. The comb and tail tend to be accentuated. There is a story behind the Portuguese cockerel. In the 13th Century a pilgrim travelling to Santiago de Compostela in north west Spain stopped at Barcelos in Portugal and was wrongly accused of stealing silver from a landowner. He was sentenced to death by hanging. After appealing to Our Lady and St James, the patron saint for protection, he announced that if he was innocent the roasted cockerel that the judge was about to eat would get up and crow. When it did, the pilgrim was acquitted. Years later he returned, so the story goes, to carve a statue of the

cockerel and since then Barcelos has become famous for its brightly painted ceramic cockerels which are sold throughout Portugal as symbols of faith, justice and good luck.

POULTRY CLUB

This is an organisation set up in the UK to oversee and administer poultry standards. It was founded in 1877 as a registered charity and exists to safeguard the interests of all pure and traditional breeds of poultry. There are a number of Breed Clubs for the more popular breeds which exist and are listed on the website: www.poultryclub.org. These are specialist clubs or societies formed to look after the interests of the particular breed and they accept membership applications. The Club runs the National Championships Show every year and is the guardian of The British Poultry Standards book published by Blackwell Science, now in its sixth edition.

POULTRY MANIA

Poultry keeping for eggs and meat became hugely popular in Britain in the 1850s. Punch Magazine was moved to label the age Poultry Mania. Its starting point was the Victorians' fascination with size – particularly if the object, was remarkably larger than the norm. As Lewis Wright remarked, remembering the heady days when the newly imported Cochin fowls amazed everyone who saw them: '... the Cochins came like giants upon the scene; they were seen, and they conquered. The few people who were first tempted to the shows went home and told with wonder that they had seen fowls as large as ostriches which nearly blew the roof off with their awful crow ...'

See also Cochins, Victoria, Wright's book of Poultry

PREDATORS

Apart from the obvious and most dangerous of predators, the fox
(see separate entry), the less likely but vicious and determined
badger (see separate entry) attacks and eats hens. Mink, living
near rivers and operating day and night, can catch and eat chicken.
Many breeds of dogs, used to killing game, can also be a major
danger to chickens, easily decimating small flocks. If a neighbour's
dog kills hens on private land then a case may be brought against
the owners. If chickens are wandering on to public land then it is a
different matter. Dogs can of course be trained to leave hens well
alone. Cats can and do kill chicks. Rats can kill chicks as can
sparrowhawks and weasels. Rats also steal and eat eggs as do
magpies.

PREENING AND THE PREEN GLAND (Uropygeal Gland)

Hens and cockerels preen themselves using their beaks at least
once a day to sort out their feathers. They use a gland located at
the base of the tail which produces a special oil secretion for the
conditioning or preening of feathers. This oil in their feathers acts
as a waterproof jacket, preventing rain from seeping through to
the skin.

PROLAPSE

This may occur as a result of straining to lay too large an egg or
because a pullet starts laying eggs before its body is ready. The
hen's bottom will look lower than usual because the vent muscles
are pushed out. A red mass of tissue will be seen pushing out through
the vent. The area can be bathed or some Vaseline applied and
then the tissue needs to be firmly pressed back in with a warm
piece of flannel.

PROVERBS AND SAYINGS

Eggy Ones

'A chicken is just an egg's way of making another egg' (Samuel Butler).

As sure as eggs is eggs = absolutely certain.

A bad egg = a hopeless, worthless person.

He that would have eggs must endure the clucking of the hen.

I have other eggs to fry = other plans.

Have egg on one's face = to be left looking silly.

Good in parts – Like the curate's egg – this is from a story in Punch Magazine about a Curate who was asked by a senior member of the church if his breakfast egg was okay. He replied that it was good in parts rather than offend by saying it was bad.

Put all one's eggs in one basket = to rely on the success of one plan or decision.

Teach one's grandmother to suck eggs = to try and show someone more experienced how to do something they can already do.

Tread or walk on eggs = eggs are fragile so this is used when one has to advance very carefully.

You cannot make an omelette without breaking eggs.

Innocent as a new-laid egg.

Eggs and oaths are easily broken.

As good an addled egg as an idle bird.

Better half an egg than an empty shell.

Hens like to lay where they see an egg. This is a Dutch Proverb and very true.

What's that got to do with the price of eggs? = a retort to an irrelevant suggestion – this was originally an American phrase, the English equivalent being 'the price of fish'.

Like as two eggs = exactly alike from Shakespeare's *Winter's Tale* 'They say we are almost alike as eggs'.

Show him an egg and instantly the whole air is full of feathers = a sanguine man who is counting his chickens before they are hatched.

Cockerel Related – Most of these are self-explanatory

Every cock will crow upon his own dunghill = everyone is confident when on home ground.

Don't crow so loud, rooster, you might lay an egg! = stop boasting.

A servant and a cock should be kept but one year.

If a cock goes crowing to bed, he will certainly rise with a watery head.

If the cock moults before the hen, we shall have weather thick and thin, if the hen moults before the cock, we shall have weather hard as a rock.

There's many a good cock come out of a tattered bag – this is a cockfighting simile and was used by a farmer whose buildings were falling down but his stock was in good condition.

Cock of the walk = the most important person in a group – the 'Walk' was the pen in which fighting cocks were bred and cared for.

Live like fighting cocks – fighting cocks get the best food.

This beats cockfighting = more exciting and enthralling than cockfighting.

That cock won't fight = a plan that won't work or a person in a dispute refuses to fight back.

Show a clean pair of heels = remove oneself from a scene as soon as possible – refers to a cowardly cockerel who runs away without striking a blow, showing his heels or spurs unstained with blood.

To make someone's hackles rise = make someone very angry.
The hackles are the long feathers on a cockerel's neck which rise when he's angry and ready for a fight.

'Let us agree not to step on each other's feet', said the cock to the horse.

He was like a cock who thought the sun had risen to hear him crow. (George Eliot)

Hen Related

Jerusalem, Jerusalem that kills the prophets, and stones those who are sent to her! How often would I have gathered your children together, even as a hen gathers her chickens under her wings, and you would not! (Matthew 23:27 *The Bible*)

Like a hen on a hot griddle = very nervous and agitated.

Henpecked = when a man is ruled by his wife – hens do sometimes peck feathers off cockerels.

Like a hen with one chicken = over-protective of one's only child.

Count one's chickens before they are hatched = make plans before something is finalised.

Chickens come home to roost = when something bad happens as a result of an action – this is from a motto in Robert Southey's poem *The Curse of Kehama* – 'Curses are like young chickens, they always come home to roost.' It can be traced back to Chaucer's *Parson's Tale* (1390) which is a variation –'Curses are like a bird that returns again to his own nest'.

Which came first – the chicken or the egg? = Sometimes impossible to tell which happened first and caused the other.

No spring chicken = someone who has aged.

To chicken out = to get out of something through cowardice.

Fat hens are ill layers.

It is a sad house where the hen crows loudest.

A whistling woman and a crowing hen are neither fit for God nor men – this was originally from a Scottish proverb – a crooning cow, a crowing hen and a whistling maid boded never luck to a house.

One chick can keep a hen busy.

A sitting hen never grows fat.

If you burn egg-shells the hens will cease to lay.

It is a bad hen that eats at home and lays away.

To take someone under one's wings = to look after someone.

To clip someone's wing = to tame someone and prevent him/her from becoming too powerful.

To feather one's nest = to make or save money for oneself at someone else's expense.

It's an ill bird that fouls its own nest = to speak badly of one's own family to strangers.

To smooth someone's ruffled feathers = to calm someone down who has had his pride injured or become upset over something.

To make the feathers fly = to start an argument which results in a fight.

Sociable as chickens in a coop.

Proud or fussy as a hen with one chick.

Cross as a setting hen.

Scarce as a hen's teeth = scarce as a hen doesn't have teeth.

The chicken is the country's but the city eats it. (George Herbert)

It may be the cock that crows, but it is the hen that lays the egg. (Margaret Thatcher)

PUB NAMES AND SIGNS

There are a number of pubs named The Cock Tavern, especially in London, often after the fact that cockfighting had taken place in the yard. There is a sign at Stroud Green in Essex which depicts a Leghorn cockerel. It is known that The Cock and Lion in London W1 was originally called The Lion – the Cock was added to commemorate the cockpit which was just outside the pub. The Cockpit in London EC4 where cockfights were made illegal in 1849 has retained its former 'viewing gallery'.

The Fighting Cocks in St Albans is thought to date from the 17th Century and takes the form of the original cockpit where the fighting cocks were let loose on one another. There are several other pubs called The Fighting Cocks in towns or villages across Britain from Winfarthing, near Diss in East Anglia to one in Birmingham, Durham, Kingston-upon-Thames, Rotherham, Bradford, Horton Kirby near Dartford in Kent and one in Godshill, near Fordingbridge, Hampshire. In Dispey near Stockport there is a pub named The Dandy Cock – in that area this is the dialectical name for the male bantam. The Cock and Trumpet in Hartshill, Stoke-on-Trent was so named because the cock and trumpet were closely associated in Elizabethan times, as shown in Shakespeare's Hamlet: 'I have heard/the cock, that is the trumpet to the morn. (See also Cockerel stories).

The Cock Inn in Stony Stratford (now The Cock Hotel) was responsible for the development of the nursery rhyme *Ride a Cock Horse to Banbury Cross* – travellers hired a horse at The Cock in Stony Stratford in order to ride to Banbury (this is only one theory – cock-horse could have just meant a high-spirited horse). There are quite a few Cock Inns – to name a few there is The Cock Inn in Barford and also in Drayton in Norfolk, one in Roade,

Northampton, The Cock Inn in Werrington, near Peterborough, The Cock in Phoenix Road, Euston in London, one in Wivelsfield Green, Haywards Heath and there is a Cock Inn in Luddesdowne, near Gravesend in Kent. There is a Black Cock Inn on Caerphilly Mountain in Wales. The Travelling Hen in Pontshill near Ross-on-Wye used to be a pub but closed 20 years ago (see Travelling Hen).

The Wyandotte Pub in Kenilworth has a sign displaying the Wyandotte breed. The story goes that John Boddington who built the pub wrote to his eldest son in America who suggested Wyandotte, the name of the town in Michigan where he lived. This was also the name of an Indian tribe and in the 1880s gave its name to the Wyandotte breed of domestic fowl.

The Three Cocks pub at Tetbury in Gloucestershire shows two cockerels pecking corn and a third as a weather-vane on a church steeple. There is a pub in Sholver Green, Oldham called The Pullet. Several pubs are called Hen and Chickens – there is one in Bristol, and one in Southwater, near Horsham, Surrey called Hen and Chicken – Hen and Chickens meant different things – for example in the late 19th Century it applied to a children's game but it was also the name used for large and small pewter pots mixed together. The Cock and Hen is a pub in Fulham, London. The Tappit Hen in Aberdeen is so named after a hen which is topped – i.e. with a crest – but also refers to a drinking vessel with a knobbed lid – the slim neck and broad body give it a hen-like shape and the lid is the crest.

PULLET

A pullet is a young hen usually up to the end of her first year of laying.

R

RARE BREED POULTRY

A number of breeds are listed by the Rare Breeds Survival Trust. Those categorised as critical include Ancona, Andalusian, Campine, Croad Langshan, Hamburgh, Modern Game, Modern Langshan, Nankin, Rosecomb, Sultan, and White Sussex. Also included are three of the autosexing breeds: Brussbar, Legbar and Welbar. Those categorised as endangered are Marsh Daisy, Old English Pheasant Fowl, Old English Game, Orpington (not the Buff) Scots Grey and Sebright.

RATS

Rats live everywhere in towns and the countryside, wherever there may be a source of food. Despite this, potential chicken keepers and their neighbours tend to be concerned about rats. Rat runs may be seen around hen houses that lead to hedges or compost heaps, holes or fresh mounds of earth. Rats urinate as they run so the vegetation will be destroyed in their wake. The rats will run at top speed along these paths as they hate open space. To deter rats food should be kept slightly off the ground and all feeders put away at night. Keep all chicken food in dustbins. Rats will kill chicks and steal eggs but won't be able to harm fully grown chickens. To kill rats traps or bait boxes can be used. Poison is placed inside the bait boxes – the poison is a mixture of kibbled wheat with green coloured bits. Rats usually die in their holes.

RECORDS

The longest recorded flight of a chicken is 13 seconds and a distance travelled of 301½ feet (which is just over 90 metres).

In June 2009 it was reported that a chicken in northern India had laid a giant egg weighing 162g, setting the national record. A farm owner in the Indian state of Punjab said that the record holder is an unnamed 10-month-old Lohmann Brown chicken who weighs 1.25kg. 'This came as a surprise. In general, these chickens lay eggs weighing between 50g and 60g,' he said. The egg is 10cm long and has a diameter of 5cm. It is said the world's largest chicken egg, which weighed 198g and was 9.4cm long, was discovered in the Chinese province of Jiangshu.

The maximum number of eggs laid by one bird in one year was 361 – they were laid by a Black Orpington called Princess Te Kawan. This may now have been superseded as there are rumours that an Australorp has laid 364 eggs in one year. There are no verified records.

The maximum number of yolks found in one egg is apparently nine.

Predictably China has the most chickens, estimated to be more than three billion.

There are more chickens in the world than any other domesticated bird, and there is more than one chicken for every human on earth.

RED JUNGLE FOWL See Jungle Fowl

RED MITE

Red mite live and breed in crevices in hen houses and are carried by wild birds. At night they run along the perches and up the chicken's leg where they suck blood from the flesh. They don't

live on the bird but can be spotted in the hen house during the day – they will be red if they have recently sucked blood, otherwise they will be grey. The chickens affected will look jaundiced through losing blood and may stop laying. Sprays such as poultry shield, smite or duramitex will kill red mite. Ant powder can be effective; a blow torch or pressure washer will destroy them.

RHODE ISLAND RED

The Rhode Island Red (RIR) is probably our best known breed. For most of the 20th Century it was the RIR along with first crosses (i.e. with Sussex) that made up about 50% of Britain's laying stock. Nearly all of today's brown egg-laying hybrids have at least one RIR parent. It originated in America on the farms of the Rhode Island Province. In 1854, in Adamsville, Little Compton William Tripp obtained a big Malay cockerel that had arrived from a south east Asian port. He ran it with his hens and found the resulting progeny was laying bigger eggs. John Macomber who lived in Massachusetts became interested and the two men worked together crossbreeding and using Cochin China hens. The offspring was then crossed with light Brahmas, Plymouth Rocks and Brown Leghorns. They were first exhibited in 1880 in South Massachusetts and in 1909 the British Rhode Island Red Club was established. In 1925 a granite monument was erected in Adamsville to honour the breed:

TO COMMEMORATE THE BIRTHPLACE OF THE RHODE ISLAND RED BREEDING FOWL WHICH WAS ORIGINATED NEAR THIS LOCATION. RED FOWLS WERE BRED EXTENSIVELY BY THE FARMERS OF THIS DISTRICT AND LATER NAMED 'RHODE ISLAND REDS' AND BROUGHT

*INTO NATIONAL PROMINENCE BY THE POULTRY
FANCIERS. THIS TABLET IS PLACED BY THE RHODE
ISLAND RED CLUB OF AMERICA WITH CONTRIBUTIONS
OF RHODE ISLAND RED BREEDERS THROUGHOUT THE
WORLD ON LAND DONATED BY DEBORAH T.
MANCHESTER.*

The breed has been one of the most popular in this country for all
purposes especially in the past when people kept hens for meat as
well as for eggs. The breed was imported to Britain around 1900.
It has yellow skin and legs, is a heavy breed in large fowl and
bantam size, lays very well, does not go broody easily and the
eggs vary from light to dark brown.
See Brown Eggs versus White Eggs

ROSECOMB BANTAM

The Rosecomb is an old rare breed of bantam, which originated in
Great Britain but little is known about its history. It has a large rose
comb with striking white earlobes and wattles. The males have
long sickle tail feathers and the wings are pointed downwards so
that the tips almost reach the floor and the back is one long elegant
curve from neck to tail. Rosecombs can be black, white or blue
and are bred mainly for showing. Hens lay white eggs.

S

SADDLES, POULTRY

It is possible to buy a poultry saddle which can be attached by using straps under the hen's wings and this will protect her from being damaged by an over-zealous cockerel. It is the claws and spurs of the cockerel which pull out the feathers on the hens' backs, making them sore. These saddles can also be used on hens at the bottom of the pecking order who are being bullied by other hens.

SALLY HENNY PENNY

Sally Henny Penny is the only hen character appearing in Beatrix Potter's tales. She features in *The Tale of Ginger and Pickles* and takes over the running of the shop. The story ends 'Sally Henny Penny gets rather flustered when she tries to count out change, and she insists on being paid cash; but she is quite harmless. And she has laid in a remarkable assortment of bargains. There is something to please everybody.'

SCALY LEG MITE

The scaly leg mite lives under the scales of the bird's leg. It is contagious and can be seen in birds of all ages. It may originate from the litter on the floor of the hen house. The scales on the legs become rough, and a chalk-like concretion is formed, which accumulates both between and over the scales. It is intensely irritating

to the bird and once developed may make the bird lame and unable to perch. The problem is relatively easy to cure and there are several different treatments that can be tried. Surgical spirit can be painted on the legs with a small paintbrush once a week for five weeks and is usually effective. Other treatments include scaly cream which is available in pet shops (used for budgies with scaly face). Eucalyptus oil, which is an organic treatment and must be rubbed into the legs every few weeks. The legs can be scrubbed with paraffin (an old fashioned remedy) using an old toothbrush (one treatment should be enough). Dipping the legs in linseed oil, which reduces the irritation, softens the scales and promotes healing but this treatment needs repeating. Vaseline or petroleum jelly gently rubbed into the legs can help.

SCOTS DUMPY

Despite being bred in Scotland for over a hundred years and the fact that it had probably been around much longer than that, this breed nearly became extinct. Originally known as Crawlers and Creepers because of their very short legs, other names for them include Go-Laighs and Bakies. Fowls of this description were described as early as 1678 in Britain. Similar birds have existed since 900AD and were probably brought to Britain by Phoenician traders. They are available as large fowl and bantams, in black, cuckoo, white, brown, gold and silver. Hens lay white eggs. Scots Dumpies were used by the Picts as ambush alarms because of their superior hearing; their short legs and inability to wander too far made them perfect free rangers for Scottish crofts.

SCOTS GREY

This is a rare, light soft-feathered breed, in large fowl and bantam size, which originated in Scotland over 200 years ago. Known as a cottager's fowl, it was admired for its hardiness and thrived in cold weather. Scots Greys are cuckoo-coloured and hens lay white eggs.

SEBRIGHT BANTAM

Sebrights are true bantams (with no large fowl counterparts) and one of the oldest British varieties. The breed was developed by Sir John Sebright in the early 1800s.
They are very small and slender, carrying their wings low and with prominent tails. Hens and cockerels have similar plumage with rose combs and can be gold or silver in colour. Hens lay small white eggs.

SELBORNE, THE NATURAL HISTORY OF

Some chicken-related extracts by Gilbert White:

... No inhabitants of a yard seem possessed of such a variety of expression and so copious a language as common poultry. Take a chicken of four or five days old, and hold it up to a window where there are flies, and it will immediately seize its prey, with little twitterings of complacency; but if you tender it a wasp or a bee, at once its note becomes harsh, and expressive of disapprobation and a sense of danger. When a pullet is ready to lay she intimates the event by a joyous and easy soft note. Of all the occurrences of

their life that of laying seems to be the most important; for no sooner has a hen disburdened herself, than she rushes forth with a clamorous kind of joy, which the cock and the rest of his mistresses immediately adopt. The tumult is not confined to the family concerned, but catches from yard to yard, and spreads to every homestead within hearing, till at last the whole village is in an uproar. As soon as a hen becomes a mother her new relation demands a new language; she then runs clocking and screaming about, and seems agitated as if possessed. The father of the flock has also a considerable vocabulary; if he finds food, he calls a favourite concubine to partake; and if a bird of prey passes over, with a warning voice he bids his family beware. The gallant chanticleer has, at command, his amorous phrases, and his terms of defiance. But the sound by which he is best known is his crowing: by this he has been distinguished in all ages as the countryman's clock or larum, as the watchman that proclaims the divisions of the night. Thus the poet elegantly styles him: ... the crested cock, whose clarion sounds the silent hours.

... A neighbouring gentleman one summer had lost most of his chickens by a sparrowhawk, that came gliding down between a faggot-pile and the end of his house to the place where the coops stood. The owner, inwardly vexed to see his flock thus diminishing, hung a setting net adroitly between the pile and the house, into which the caitiff dashed and was entangled. Resentment suggested the law of retaliation; he therefore clipped the hawk's wings, cut off his talons, and, fixing a cork on his bill, threw him down among the brood-hens. Imagination cannot paint the scene that ensued; the expressions that fear, rage, and revenge inspired, were new, or at least such as had been unnoticed before: the exasperated matrons upbraided, they execrated, they insulted, they triumphed. In

a word, they never desisted from buffeting their adversary till they had torn him in an hundred pieces.

... On the 14th the writer was obliged to be much abroad; and thinks he never before or since has encountered such rugged Siberian weather. Many of the narrow roads were now filled above the tops of the hedges; through which the snow was driven into most romantic and grotesque shapes ... The poultry dared not stir out of their roosting-places; for cocks and hens are so dazzled and confounded by the glare of snow that they would soon perish without assistance.

SENSES

Chickens have very good sight and hearing. They can focus on small things within a range of five metres. They can view larger things up to 50 metres away. They see using their left and right eyes alternately and this is why they tend to walk in a zigzag fashion. They can see bright colours but are almost blind in the dark unlike ducks who can see well in darkness. Chickens make about 30 different sounds. They can perceive vibrations, feeling them in the ground and in the atmosphere. A chicken can also be hypnotised by tucking the head into its wing and rocking it gently from side to side. If put down the chicken will remain hypnotised for 30 seconds. Hens respond to being touched on their backs usually by going into a sexual crouch.

It is thought that chickens have a good sense of smell – they do reject sour and salty food so presumably can smell it. There is a small pair of air holes towards the upper end of a bird's beak which is the chicken's version of nostrils. Their sense of taste is thought to be rather poor in comparison.

See also Clucking

SERAMA

This is the world's smallest bantam and a relatively new breed. It was developed in the Malaysian state of Kelantan, apparently from crossing Japanese bantams and some local Malaysian bantams. The birds are tiny and must weigh less than 450g. The breed was named after the Thai King Rama, because of its proud upright carriage. The cockerel in particular carries himself very erect, with an upright tail, short body and protruding breast. Hens not surprisingly lay very small eggs. A breed club has been set up and was officially recognised by the Poultry Club in 2008.

SHAKE BAGS

Shake bags were over-sized fighting cocks, originally called turn-pokes. These cocks were released by turning the bag or poke upside down on the pit. Over-sized cocks were difficult to match and did not fight well in the pit, being less nimble and strong than those of medium size.

SHAMO

The Shamo breed was originally imported to Japan from Thailand and the name was a corruption of Siam, the old name for Thailand. The Shamo is a game fowl and in Japan this was the ultimate fighting cock – it has an upright carriage with a powerful and fierce stance.

SHELL-LESS EGGS

Shell-less or soft-shelled eggs with just the membrane around the egg can be quite a common problem especially with hybrids. This may happen in young pullets – the egg goes down through the oviduct so quickly that there is no time for the shell to be made.

Sometimes pullets are adjusting to their new egg-laying functions with just the first few eggs being shell-less. If the egg has a very thin shell, there may not be enough calcium or vitamin D in the diet so crushed oystershells should be given. If a hen is still laying soft-shelled eggs after two or three weeks, it may be due to some inherent weakness in the strain which does not allow proper assimilation of calcium or an inherent malfunctioning of the reproductive tract – this could have been caused by infectious bronchitis or another disease when the hen was younger or intensive breeding may have led to malformed ovaries.

See also Egg-shells

SICILIAN BUTTERCUP

This breed originated in Sicily and arrived in America in the 1800s. It was first imported to Britain by Mrs Colbeck in 1912. The distinguishing feature on this bird is the saucer-shaped cup comb. Coloured in gold or silver, bantams are available as well as large fowl. Hens are good layers of white eggs.

SILKIE

Silkies originated in Asia, some believe in India, others think in China or Japan. The breed may have been discovered by Marco Polo (1254 – 1324) near the south Chinese town of Quelinsu – he mentions in his book about the Orient 'exotic oriental chickens that have hair like a cat, are black and lay the best of eggs'.

Aldrovandi describes Silkies as white as snow with wool like sheep. Their fluffy look led to the bizarre rumour that they were produced by crossing a rabbit and chicken and thus were sometimes referred to as rabbit-fowl. Silkies are covered in fine, silky fluff rather than feathers. The wings are also covered in this fluff which prevents Silkies from flying. They have a unique feature in that their flesh is almost black with black bones and skin. Colours range from blue, gold and black to white and partridge. Crested with a mulberry comb and wattles and earlobes preferably turquoise, they have feathered legs and five toes. Silkies are classified as a light soft-feathered large fowl but a small bantam version has been created which is docile and therefore popular with children. Silkies are famous for their broodiness and well known for making fantastic surrogate mothers. They will take on other hens' chicks, even when a few days old. In times gone by, before incubators existed, Silkies were used as natural incubators by breeders not only of chickens, but also of pheasant, partridge and duck.

SICKLES
Sickles are the long pointed feathers in a cock's tail.

SITTERS
The best sitters are Silkies closely followed by Pekins. The heavy breeds are mainly the ones that sit. These include Barnevelder, Brahma, Cochin, Dorking, Faverolles, Houdan, Modern and Old English Game, Marans, New Hampshire Red, Orpington, Plymouth Rock, Rhode Island Red, Scots Dumpy, Sussex and Wyandotte. They lay mainly tinted (light brown) or brown eggs.
See also Non-sitters

SOFT-FEATHERED BREEDS
Most breeds apart from the Game breeds are soft-feathered

SOFT-SHELLED EGGS see Shell-less eggs

SPACE
All chickens like space and the more they get the better. Hens love to peck at grass, scratch in areas of bare soil, piles of leaves etc. Understandably hens have to be confined where there is a danger of predators but if they can be let out for at least part of the day this will give them some much needed freedom. Electric fencing can be used to keep foxes out; arks have attached runs and can be moved to new patches of grass. Fences around runs should be dug at least 30cm into the ground to stop badgers and foxes burrowing underneath.

SPANISH BREEDS Named after places
The Andalusian breed owes its name to the province of Andalusia and the Minorca originated on the island of Menorca, one of the Balearic Islands off the east coast of Spain. It is thought that the Minorca arrived in the west of England possibly as early as 1780 when Spanish and French prisoners were interned there and, after peace was declared, became naturalised Englishmen and imported the Minorcas. There is also a specific Spanish breed, black with white face and hens lay large, white eggs.
See separate entries under individual breeds

SPECKLEDY
A Speckledy is a hybrid hen based on the Marans and thus a layer of reasonably dark brown eggs.

 SPECKLEDY HEN, THE

The Speckledy Hen is the hen in the story of the same name by Alison Uttley who slips away from the noisy farmyard to find somewhere quiet to lay her eggs. She makes her nest in a large oak tree and by and by hatches 10 chicks. But nearby a fox is waiting … Her friends have to save her and consult Wise Owl who suggests that someone reads a story to keep the fox occupied. Fuzzypeg, the hedgehog obliges and Speckledy Hen and her chicks make their escape to rejoin all their friends in the farmyard. The Speckledy Hen also features in other stories in *The Little Grey Rabbit* series.

SPENT HENS

Spent hens are battery hens that have laid intensely for a year and are ready for slaughter. A small proportion of these hens are now being rescued; the rest are slaughtered and their flesh is used in low quality processed foods such as soup, pies and baby food.

SPURS

These are horny sharp growths that grow on the inside legs of cockerels. Artificial metal spurs were used in cockfighting and were first introduced in the late 1600s. The cockerel's natural spurs were filed down and these metal spurs were attached with leathers around the legs as they would incur more serious injuries. Silver spurs apparently proved less fatal than spurs of steel.

 SQUARE EGG , THE by Saki (1924)

This was a short story about a man who says that he has produced a breed of hens that lay square eggs. He had gone off to war and

left the business in the charge of his aunt who now refuses to give him any of the profits. He wishes to sue his aunt and asks his friend for some money. The friend says he will visit the farm and the story ends – 'And if you find that what I have told you about the square eggs is true, Monsieur, what then?' 'I shall marry your aunt.'

STREET NAMES

Many streets were named after the cock in areas where cockfighting had taken place. Cock Lane is an alleyway in London near the Smithfield Market. Cockspur Street near Charing Cross in London is named after the shops there that used to produce artificial spurs for fighting cocks. There is also a Cockspur Street in Liverpool named because there was once a cockpit in the street. Cock Roads abound especially in the south of England – to name a few: there is a Cock Road in Rowde and in Horningsham, both villages in Wiltshire, a Cock Road in Kingswood, Bristol, a Cock Road in Hanham, one in Wimborne, Dorset and one in Little Maplestead, Essex, in Buckland Dinham, Somerset and one in Cotton, Suffolk. There is a Three Cocks Lane in Gloucester. Cockshut or Cockshutt Lane is a name that crops up in villages. There is also a village called Cockshutt in Shropshire. Cock's Shut was a country word for twilight as the time when cockerels retired to their roosts so this was presumably how the street name evolved. Several Councils across Britain want to change the names of such streets as they are politically incorrect by today's standards and regarded as offensive.

SULMTALER

The Sulmtaler breed originated in Austria in an area which included the valley of Sulm (tal – valley). This heavy breed was developed

with crossings of Cochins, Houdans and Dorkings. The Sulmtaler is regarded as a good utility breed because it is hardy, fast growing and easy to fatten up. It is bred in one colour with the hens and cockerels varying in colour – cockerels are black-breasted red and hens are wheaten. Hens lay light brown eggs. Bantam versions are available.

SULTAN

The Sultan originated in Turkey in the Sultan of Constantinople's palace garden. Miss Elizabeth Watts of Hampstead brought a crate of Sultans back to England in 1854 and today's Sultans are descended from these. They are white with feathered feet, five toes, crests and muffling and available as large fowl or bantams. Hens and cockerels look very similar except the cockerel has a larger comb and tail feathers. Hens lay white eggs.

SUMATRA

The Sumatra breed originated in Indonesia and is a beautiful bird with an all black appearance (faces, beaks and legs are black) and feathers have a bottle-green sheen to their blackness. With a large flowing tail and a pheasant-like appearance it looks very elegant. The tail feathers of the cockerel brush along the ground as both hens and cockerels are short but with long bodies. Hens are prolific layers of white eggs and make good sitters. Large fowl and bantam versions are available.

SUNBATHING

Chickens love to sunbathe – they lie on one side and spread out their uppermost wing. They need their vitamin D just as we do.

SUSSEX

This is an old breed derived from the Old Sussex fowls which were bred in Victorian times for their meat and eggs. The oldest variety is in fact the Speckled Sussex. The Light Sussex was developed using Brahmas, Cochins and Dorkings in the south east of England. Old English Game were used in the make up of the Browns and Buffs and were developed during the twenties. During the war Light Sussexes along with Rhode Island Reds seem to have been popular breeds to keep for the dual purpose of eggs and meat. Colours vary from brown, red, speckled, silver and white but light and buff are probably the most common colours. The Sussex is a heavy soft-feathered breed available as bantams or as large fowl. The Sussex is a calm, friendly breed and easily tamed. The hens are really good layers of tinted eggs and tend to lay in the winter as well.

T

TEMPERA

Tempera, also known as egg tempera, is a permanent fast drying painting medium consisting of coloured pigments mixed with a water-soluble binding agent such as egg yolk removed from its sac. It is noted for its strong, translucent colours, and can be thinned with water. Tempera also refers to the paintings done in this medium. A form of tempera was used in ancient Egypt, and egg tempera was the foremost medium for panel painting in late medieval and early Renaissance Europe. It was gradually replaced in popularity by oils from the late 15th Century onwards. Tempera paintings are very long lasting and examples from the first centuries AD still exist.

TOTTENHAM HOTSPUR FOOTBALL CLUB

A fighting cockerel on a ball is the symbol for this football club. The cockerel wears a pair of spurs and has been the crest and shield of the Club since 1901.

TRANSYLVANIAN NAKED NECK

A rare breed from Romania, this is an unattractive bird with its naked neck extending down to the crop, but an excellent forager. Hens are good layers of tinted eggs. This is a rare breed available most commonly in black, white or cuckoo in large fowl or bantams.

TRAPNEST

This is a special nest box with a door attached. The door falls shut

when the hen enters the nest, leaving her trapped until she is released and a note of her achievement is made. The trapnest was used in the past by commercial breeders so that they could understand which hens were laying which eggs.

TRAVELLING HEN INN

Formerly known as The New Inn in Pontshill, Herefordshire, the name was changed in 1965 to The Travelling Hen to commemorate the resident hen, Clara, who seemed to have an unusual desire to travel. In the early 1960s Clara, the Rhode Island Red, often went missing from home for weeks on end. The story goes that the hen was found on the back axle of a lorry that had parked in the car park overnight and which then travelled from Pontshill to Birmingham. She made the return journey in the driver's cab and laid an egg. The local tale is that the same hen hitched a ride on the same lorry to Cardiff and laid an egg on the way home. The New Inn was therefore renamed in honour of the hen who was actually present at the ceremony. In another version of the story the hen made a nest on top of a petrol tanker, laid a clutch of eggs and hatched them out as the lorry made several long-distance journeys. The Travelling Hen Inn has been closed for over 20 years and is now The Country Cookshop.

TRIO

A trio is a cockerel with two hens and is the term used in the sale and showing of chickens.

TUZO BANTAM

The Tuzo is a true bantam originating from Japan. It is a rare breed and is a game fowl with an upright carriage, similar to an Asil.

V

VALERIE

Valerie became famous through featuring on *The Natural History of Chickens* which was made in America in 2000 and shown in Britain on BBC4 in 2007. New Englander Janet Bonney finds Valerie, one of her wayward chickens, frozen to death during a blizzard. After bringing the frigid fowl inside, Janet detects a faint heartbeat and improvises mouth-to-beak CPR. Valerie's astonishing recovery got the attention of the press worldwide.

VENT

The vent is the orifice at the back end of the bird through which the egg passes out but also through which excreta is expelled. The vent of a laying hen will be larger than a non-layer, moist and crescent shaped.

See also Cloaca

VICTOIRE

Victoire is a cockerel accused of crowing in the middle of the night, who won a court case in France in 2007. A 70 year old woman and her son living in the village of Wittersdorf, in Alsace went to court accusing the cockerel of ruining their lives by constantly crowing from 3am and demanded 1,500 euros for loss of sleep. But the judge ruled in favour of the cockerel and the family had to pay 400 euros for the cost of the trial. The lawyer stated: 'In the

countryside there has to be a certain level of tolerance. This is a logical common sense judgment.'

See also Crowing, George, Corky

VICTORIA, QUEEN

Queen Victoria's poultry house at Windsor

Queen Victoria was a real poultry enthusiast when she was young. She was presented with a crate of Cochins which came off boats from Canton in south China in 1843. In 1846 Queen Victoria exhibited three of her birds at the Royal Dublin Society's Show and won the gold medal. They were evidently crossed with the Dorking as these birds had five toes. The hens were subsequently presented to the Lord Lieutenant of Ireland, Lord Heytesbury. Queen Victoria had a poultry house built at Windsor and was also sent nine Brahmas (then known as grey Shanghais) by an American breeder, George Burnham in 1852.

See also Brahma, Cochin, Poultry Mania

The Brahmas presented to Queen Victoria

VORWERK

The Vorwerk was developed in Germany in 1900 by Oskar Vorwerk and is classed as a rare breed. Vorwerks make excellent hens for the garden because the large fowl are of medium size, attractive and thrive very well on less food than other breeds. Bantams are also available but predictably quite small. Vorwerks are buff coloured with black belted marking which means the neck and tail feathers are black. They are alert, very active and excellent foragers. They lay white eggs and go broody fairly easily. Vorwerks are good flyers so do not usually like to be confined.

W

WATTLES

Wattles are the two red fleshy appendages hanging below the beak. Hens have small wattles, cockerels have much larger ones. The wattles are there to cool the chicken down – blood circulates from the comb to the wattles and lowers the bird's temperature during hot weather.

WEATHERCOCK

The weathercock or weather vane is an instrument for showing the direction of the wind and often features the traditional cockerel design. From the Old English word fane, which means flag or banner, we get the more common word vane. It is an ornament placed at the highest point of a building and the cockerel signifies the need for watchfulness. In the 9th Century the Pope called on every European church to show a cock on its steeple or dome as a reminder of the prophecy Jesus made that the cock would not crow the morning after the Last Supper until Peter had denounced him three times.

There is a scene on the Bayeux Tapestry showing a craftsman attaching a cockerel to the spire on Westminster Abbey. The oldest weathercock still functioning on top of a church is in Ottery St Mary, Devon and dates back to 1340. An interesting story comes from Austria and is about the weathercock on St Stephen's Cathedral in Vienna. In the Middle Ages Knight von Schlezer was

captured and enslaved on his way back from Turkey to his wife in
Austria. After five years he had a dream that his wife was about to
marry another Knight – he cried out 'I must be in Vienna tomorrow
even if the Devil takes me'. Instantly the Devil arrived astride a
cockerel to take the Knight to Austria but demanded the Knight's
soul in return. They flew off but the Knight took hold of his crucifix
and committed his soul to God. As the Cathedral came into view
the Devil realised he had lost power over his victim and cast him
and the cockerel into the Danube. They were rescued in time for
the Knight to stop the marriage of his wife. To thank the cockerel
the Knight had an iron weathercock constructed and put on the
roof of the Cathedral where it can still be seen today.

WELSUMMER

Although Welsummers are traditionally associated with Welsum in
Holland the breed was originally created in the area along the river
Ysel, just north of Deventer. The breed was developed in the early
1900s. In its early development Barnevelders, another Dutch
breed, were used. At first these birds were called Welsumers but
when they arrived in Britain around 1928 and a Breed Club was
set up the name changed to Welsummer. A light, soft-feathered

breed, hens lay large dark brown eggs with a matt shell rather than the glossy shell of the Marans. The colour of the eggs will vary slightly depending on the strain but these are probably the darkest brown of all. Welsummers were originally all a red partridge colour – the cocks always have reddish brown mottling on their black breasts, however for some time now there has been a silver duckwing variety and a rarer gold duckwing is available too. Welsummers are active foragers so do well as free rangers. They don't lay as many eggs a year as some other breeds and are classed as non-sitters but are known to go broody, depending on the strain. Large fowl and bantams are available.

WING CLIPPING

If there is a problem with hens flying out of runs then wings can be clipped – only one wing on each bird should be clipped as the idea is to make flying impossible due to imbalance. Use kitchen scissors and cut about 7cm from where the quills go into the flesh – if one cuts too near the flesh the quills will bleed. It is the primary feathers that are cut.

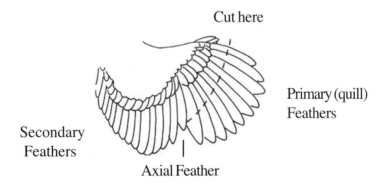

Cut here

Primary (quill) Feathers

Secondary Feathers

Axial Feather

 WISE LITTLE HEN, THE

This is a version of *The Little Red Hen* story which was made into a short Disney film (1934) and was the first to feature Donald Duck. Peter Pig and Donald Duck refuse to help Wise Little Hen who gathers corn, makes her meal and plays a trick by presenting them with a covered bowl – inside is a bottle of castor oil.

WISHBONE

The chicken's wishbone is the clavicle or collar bone and overlies the breast bone connecting the shoulders. It was customary to save the wishbone, dry it until brittle and then two people, usually children, would pull at the bone until it broke – the one winning the longer half would make a wish.

WORMS

There are six different types of worms which can live in the internal parts of chickens. Hens infected with worms will be listless and have green diarrhoea. Treat for worms with Flubenvet (available from feed suppliers) mixed into the feed. However some poultry experts say that hens should be treated for worms twice a year whether they show symptoms or not whilst others say that de-worming a healthy hen weakens the system and upsets the natural balance of helpful organisms.

WRIGHT'S BOOK OF POULTRY

This is perhaps the most famous 19th Century illustrated book on poultry with text by Lewis Wright and illustrations by JW Ludlow. Published in 1873 by Cassell, it was reprinted several times in the

late 1800s, and is now a rare and very collectable book. The book contains information on topics such as breeding, rearing, housing feeding and showing. It is particularly sought after for the illustrations. Each bird is sensitively portrayed in a natural farm or hen house setting. Some illustrations show a single bird, others show two, either the more showy males, or a pair of male and female. Some pictures specify name of breed and prizes. Some also specify owner or name of the bird. For example, Mr RB Wood's pair of Crevecoeurs won '1st prizes at Wolverhampton Birmingham (Summer Show) Spalding & Chesterfield, 1872,' and Mr Tomlinson's Buff Cochin Cock Sampson was 'winner of the Birmingham Cup in 1860 and 1861.' JW Ludlow was an ornithological artist who specialised in domestic birds. His poultry illustrations are considered classics and are widely reproduced as posters today. Lewis Wright was a Victorian author, editor and poultry, pigeon and animal expert. He played a major part in documenting old and rare breeds of poultry and recording their histories. Wright was the subject of the 2001 book *Lewis Wright and His Poultry* by Joseph Batty.

WYANDOTTE

Originally known as the 'American Seabright' or 'Seabright Cochin', the exact origin of the Wyandotte remains unknown to this day. Some say the Wyandotte was named after a tribe of American Indians – the logo for the Silver Wyandotte Club of America contains a drawing of an Indian tepee. Some say that Houdlette, one of the first Wyandotte breeders, named them after his father's ship, the Wyandotte. The silver-laced Wyandotte was the first Wyandotte variety accepted to the breed standard in 1883 in the

US. Experts believe that the original Wyandottes were bred by crossing Dark Brahmas with Spangled Hamburghs and possibly Polands. Later in the breed's history, other varieties were developed elsewhere in the United States. For example, in 1880 silver-laced Wyandottes and partridge Cochin-Browns were crossed in Wisconsin to create the golden-laced Wyandotte. The Columbian Wyandotte variety was bred by crossing white Wyandottes with Brahmas, for the 1893 Columbian Exposition in Chicago, for which it was named. The Wyandotte was introduced into Britain in the late 1800s and by the early 1900s was very popular, along with the Leghorn, as an egg-laying breed. There are several more varieties nowadays which include buff and blue-laced, partridge, Columbian and silver-pencilled. Wyandottes are a heavy, soft-feathered breed and lay tinted eggs. Bantams tend to be a good size and large fowl are very large.

Y

YOKOHAMA

The Yokohama originated in Japan and was imported into Europe in the mid 1800s supposedly shipped from the Port of Yokohama to France. The birds are famous for their incredibly long tail feathers and mainly kept as ornamental birds for showing since their tails need looking after carefully. Yokohamas are sometimes called Japanese Longtails or Phoenix in Europe. Yokohamas can be duckwing, golden or black-red, red-saddled or white in colour. Bantam versions have also been bred. Hens lay tinted eggs.

YURLOV CROWER

The Yurlov is a Russian breed which is famous for the long, sustained crow of the cockerel – the crow lasts between seven and nine seconds. The cockerel was bred in Russia at the beginning of the 20th Century for cock crowing competitions. The Yurlov, popular with a few German poultry fanciers came to western Europe only in the last 20 years. Colours vary from white, silver, scarlet, black with light yellow, golden and black. Hens make good layers.
See also Crowing